Know Your New Zealand ...

Native Plants

Lawrie Metcalf

First published in 2009 by New Holland Publishers (NZ) Ltd
Auckland • Sydney • London • Cape Town

www.newhollandpublishers.co.nz

218 Lake Road, Northcote, Auckland 0627, New Zealand
Unit 1, 66 Gibbes Street, Chatswood, NSW 2067, Australia
86–88 Edgware Road, London W2 2EA, United Kingdom
80 McKenzie Street, Cape Town 8001, South Africa

Publishing manager: Matt Turner
Editing and design: Punaromia
Cover design: Nick Turzynski, redinc
Front cover photographs, clockwise from left: mountain flax, leafless clematis,
rengarenga, akakura.
Back cover photographs, from top: karangu, raupo, glasswort, prostrate kowhai.
Contents page photographs, from left: winika, easter orchid.

Metcalf, L. J. (Lawrence James), 1928-
Know your New Zealand native plants / text and photography by Lawrie Metcalf.
Includes bibliographical references and index.
ISBN 978-1-86966-205-9
1. Endemic plants—New Zealand—Identification. 2. Endemic
plants—New Zealand—Guidebooks. I. Title.
581.993—dc 22

10 9 8 7 6 5 4 3 2 1

Colour reproduction by Pica Digital Pte Ltd, Singapore
Printed by Tien Wah Press (Pte) Ltd on paper sourced from sustainable forests.

Contents

Introduction	4
The plants described	4
Terminology	5
Distribution diagrams	5
The vegetation of New Zealand	5
Scrublands	6
Climbing plants	8
Grasslands	8
Wetlands	9
Coastal areas	9
Alpine areas	9
Plant diagrams	10
Glossary	11
Species	14
Bibliography	174
Index	174

Introduction

In most writings about New Zealand's native plants, it is the trees that appear to capture most people's imagination and claim the greatest share of attention. Possibly, that is because of their very nature, as they are, in the main, tall and magnificent; there is a great deal of legend and romance about them; they formerly provided a thriving industry; and this country was once largely covered with impressive forests.

This book is an attempt to rectify that situation and enable readers to gain an appreciation of those plants that do not qualify as trees – the shrubs, the climbers and herbs – some of which, nonetheless, can be fascinating and interesting, even though they do not have the grand stature of the tallest of our forest trees, or their aura. Within these broad groups of plants are included the inhabitants of alpine areas, scrublands, wetlands and sea coasts.

The plants described

Most of the plants described and illustrated are the more common species, which may be observed in many parts of the country, and are likely to be seen as you travel around New Zealand. Some, however, may be less common because they have a more limited distribution or are restricted to particular localities and habitats. They have mainly been included because of their interest value. A few – the two species of native hibiscus, for example – have a very limited distribution and you are only likely to see them if you are fortunate to visit the particular areas where they grow or to see them in cultivation. They have been included because they are considered to be such special plants.

For convenience, the plants described are listed according to the families to which they belong and are in currently accepted botanical order. The members of each family are also grouped together. Their scientific names include the genus (the first name) and species (the second name). Readers can see the relationships between the various species and genera and also those of closely related families.

In the side panel for each plant entry are listed a couple of key features, the scientific name, alternative names in current use (former names are given in the main text), key Maori names, and the approximate height of a mature plant.

The main entry for each species includes a description of its general appearance, habit, foliage, flowers and fruit, as well as cultural or other uses.

Terminology

In all descriptions an attempt has been made to keep botanical terminology to a minimum; however, it is not always possible to avoid the use of such terms. There are times when, for greater accuracy as well as to avoid the use of wordy phrases, something can better be expressed in one word, and such terms are deemed necessary. A glossary has been provided on pages 11–13 so that readers may be able to familiarise themselves with those terms, and some diagrams appear on page 10.

Where appropriate, common or vernacular names have been provided, but, because of the enthusiasm of some authors for coining and providing common names, there is often a plethora of common names that are not always helpful and can be confusing. Some authors simply take the scientific name and partially translate it into a common name; for example, *Pittosporum cornifolium*, which can be found in some books as 'the cornel-leaved pittosporum'. It is surely just as easy to refer to this species as *Pittosporum cornifolium* as it is to use the anglicised version. Maori vernacular names can also be confusing because they do not necessarily distinguish between similar plants that are completely different species. An obvious example is mingimingi (northern dialect) or mikimiki (southern dialect). There are at least five different species that are referred to as mingimingi or mikimiki, several having a very similar appearance, and so it really is necessary to refer to these plants by their scientific names in order that there can be no doubt as to which species is actually being discussed.

Distribution diagrams

Distribution diagrams are provided for each species so as to indicate the broader areas (in grey shading) over which a species may be present. These diagrams are not meant to be definitive and do not necessarily imply that a particular species will occur in every part of the indicated area. As not infrequently happens with the New Zealand flora, some species may have a remarkably discontinuous distribution while, depending on the part of the country, there may also be considerable distances between one sighting of a particular species and the next area where it may occur.

The vegetation of New Zealand

There are various other plant communities that are just as important as forests, yet too often they are completely ignored. As already mentioned, in the eyes of many people, it is the trees that are regarded as the glamorous film stars while the supporting actors, as all of the other plants and plant communities may be termed, barely rate a mention. They may be listed in the credits at the end of the film but they roll through so quickly that hardly anybody takes any notice.

How often do you hear somebody dismissively remark, 'It is only a piece of old manuka or kanuka scrub,' as though it was of no value whatsoever? And yet an examination of that same scrub community might reveal a whole host of interesting and even remarkable plant species.

This book is an attempt to rectify that situation so that, hopefully, more people will realise that New Zealand's plant communities are not comprised of just trees but contain a whole range of interesting plants. I recommend that those who are keen to further their knowledge contact their local botanical society and join society members on some of the many and varied field trips that are organised.

Scrublands

Scrublands or shrublands constitute those areas where multi-stemmed shrubs predominate. These scrubland areas may be inhabited naturally by such plants or they may be former forested areas that have been cleared as the result of the march of civilisation. They have since reverted to scrub as the first stage of a long journey back to once again becoming covered with forest. In this latter case the usual shrubs are most likely manuka (*Leptospermum scoparium*) or kanuka (*Kunzea ericoides*), or both. In particular, manuka and kanuka act as 'nurse plants' so that, over a period of time, they prepare the ground and provide the required conditions for the next stage of forest regeneration to be able to occur. With manuka, a period of up to 20 years or so may elapse before it reaches an age that will permit the next generation of seedling trees to become conspicuous. Kanuka takes quite a bit longer and it may be up to 50 years or more before it attains sufficient age for its canopy to open out, thus allowing the entry of more light that will permit the second generation to commence growing.

It may sound heretical, but two very weedy adventives (non-indigenous plants), gorse (*Ulex europaeus*) and broom (*Cytisus scoparius*), if left to their own devices, will also act as nurse crops, eventually allowing the regeneration of native trees and shrubs to occur. Gorse initially forms a very dense scrub through which other trees and shrubs find it very difficult to grow but, ultimately, as it becomes senescent, its growth will weaken and become open to let more light through, thus allowing the first native trees to emerge from the canopy of gorse. Once that begins to happen the fate of the gorse is sealed as more and more native trees begin to overtop it. Generally, this process will take about 20 years before the first emergent native trees appear. Broom grows more quickly and, after about 10 years, its growth will start becoming senescent and open out to allow the regeneration of native trees. Unfortunately, before that can happen, all too often the gorse or broom is burnt and so the whole process has to recommence.

Some scrublands appear to be more natural and look like they have been there for quite a long time. In some instances they could be the result of having been burnt off during the earliest years of European colonisation or they may have a far older origin, resulting from the burning off of former forest land by pre-European Maori. Climatic changes since the original burning may have helped to prevent the forest from regenerating, thus creating a more or less permanent scrubland.

Depending upon climatic and other circumstances, some shrubs are quite capable of growing into small trees and will form low forests or scrub-forests. Such scrub-forests may appear to occur more frequently in the higher rainfall regions of both main islands, although they can and do occur in drier areas.

Above the tree line, in alpine regions, there is usually a very distinct subalpine scrub comprising various species such as *Hebe*, *Olearia*, *Coprosma*, *Phyllocladus*, and *Brachyglottis*. Such scrub may also include *Chionochloa* (snow grass) as well as one or two of the larger ferns. Just above the tree line these subalpine scrublands may be up to 2 m or more tall, and can be so dense as to be almost impenetrable, but, as higher altitudes are gained, the shrubs become progressively shorter and more widely spaced, until eventually it is no longer scrubland but an association of low shrubs, grasses and alpine plants.

Scrublands that appear to be of a long-standing nature, and fairly permanent, can and do slowly and imperceptibly change so that, over a period of many years, they may in due course become forest. Possibly, the soil is very impoverished or it may be very poorly drained, perhaps because there is a hard and impervious pan over the subsoil layer, or it may be a combination of both factors. No matter what, sooner or later one or two trees may become established in such areas until eventually the trees are sufficiently numerous, causing the shrubs to weaken and die as a low forest becomes established. Such areas often occur particularly in western parts of the South Island where they are referred to as pakihi. Pakihi country can be open or barren land that is flat and poorly drained, sometimes rather swampy, and it may be vegetated initially with rushes, tangle ferns, clubmosses and perhaps with stunted manuka. In time, one or two trees may gain a foothold so that gradually they may become quite forested.

Climbing plants

New Zealand's forests, being rainforests, naturally include a good representation of climbing plants that accomplish their ascent of trees by twining (e.g. *Muehlenbeckia*), having hooked prickles that enable them to cling to the vegetation up which they are climbing (e.g. *Rubus*), holding fast to whatever their tendrils coil around (e.g. *Clematis*), clinging to their support by means of aerial roots (e.g. *Metrosideros*), or scrambling up simply by pushing their stems and branchlets up through the branches of some handy shrub or small tree. In all, there are approximately 50 plants that may be classified as climbers of some kind or another.

Such plants are often referred to as lianes (singular, liane) or lianas (singular, liana), a term usually used for woody climbing plants of tropical forests. Therefore, as some of our New Zealand climbers have their origins in tropical or subtropical forests they may truly be referred to as lianes.

While they are growing in the depths of the forest, under the canopy of the trees, many of these climbing plants do not flower well, or they may flower only sparsely, and it is only when their top-growth emerges from the overhead canopy that they are able to enjoy some sunlight and are then able to flower well. Some of these plants, such as *Muehlenbeckia australis*, are mainly inhabitants of forest margins, and in such locations they can form great smothering masses that appear to cover everything completely. Some people do not fully understand the role of *Muehlenbeckia* as a component of the forest and tend to regard it as a pest that should be eliminated.

Grasslands

It is believed that many of the grassland areas widely considered to be a natural part of the landscape, particularly along the eastern South Island and also in the south-eastern North Island, have arisen only over the past few hundred years, largely as the result of fires started by early Polynesian explorers and travellers. Such fires destroyed the forest and, possibly as the result of associated climatic change, the forest was unable to re-establish itself but was replaced by native grasses such as *Chionochloa* (snow grasses). On the lowland and lower hill country most of the grasslands were what is now referred to as low tussock grassland. This grassland comprises the shorter tussock grasses such as *Poa cita* (silver tussock) and *Festuca novae-zelandiae* (hard tussock or fescue tussock). On the higher mountain country where the large *Chionochloa* (snow tussocks) grow, those grasslands are referred to as tall tussock grasslands.

Wetlands

Wetlands are an important part of the vegetational areas of New Zealand, and yet they are also one of the most misunderstood and neglected areas, as well as being areas that have been most abused because of intensive farming and land development. Over the years, large areas of wetlands have disappeared and it is amazing, not that so many have gone, but that so many still remain.

Wetlands include not only freshwater swamps and bogs but also tidal lands around our coasts. Wetland areas also occur in higher-altitude mountain regions. Most wetland areas have distinct plant communities that may range from grasses and sedges to ferns and other small plants, distinct shrubland communities, even stunted forests and tall forest species such as the noble kahikatea (*Dacrycarpus dacrydioides*). In short, they are many and varied and play an important role in the well-being of the whole country as far as soil fertility, water conservation and general biodiversity are concerned.

Coastal areas

Around our sea coasts there is often a very interesting range of plant species, some of which may be specially adapted for growing in those areas, particularly when situated close to the sea and exposed to the influence of salt spray or periodic inundation by salt water. There are also marginal areas, just back from the high-tide mark, where there is a distinct kind of vegetation that must endure the effects of lashing salt-laden winds.

Along some coastal areas there are also sand dunes that have their own specialised plants such as pingao (*Desmoschoenus spiralis*) or silvery sand grass (spinifex or kowhangatara, *Spinifex sericeus*).

Alpine areas

Because of New Zealand's mountainous nature there are extensive alpine areas, particularly in the South Island but also in the central and southern North Island. Stewart Island also has quite large areas of alpine vegetation. Any area of vegetation above the zone of subalpine scrub is generally referred to as being alpine, although there are various kinds of vegetational zones within the alpine zone.

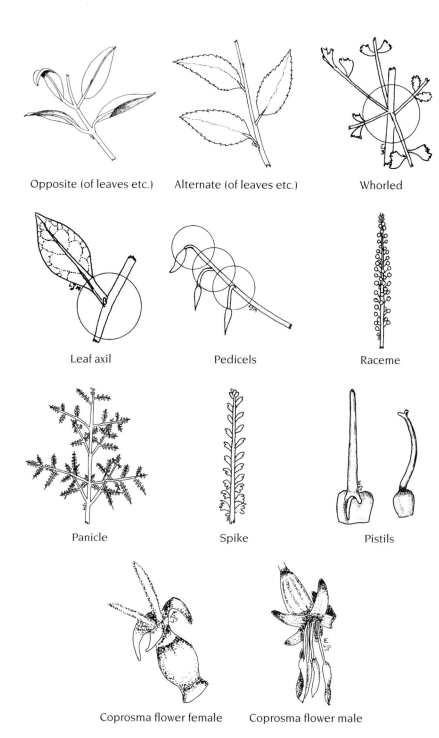

Opposite (of leaves etc.) Alternate (of leaves etc.) Whorled

Leaf axil Pedicels Raceme

Panicle Spike Pistils

Coprosma flower female Coprosma flower male

Glossary

Acute: sharply pointed.

Alternate: (leaves) placed singly along a stem or axis, not in opposite pairs.

Apex: the pointed tip or end of a leaf.

Appressed: (leaves) closely and flatly pressed against the surface of a stem.

Axil: (adjective: axillary) the upper angle, usually between leaf and stem.

Berry: a fleshy fruit containing several to many seeds but not a stone.

Compound: particularly of leaves; composed of several, more or less similar, parts (leaflets) as opposed to simple.

Corolla: the inner, usually showy whorl of floral parts, consisting of free or united petals.

Corymb: (adjective: corymbose) a more or less flat-topped raceme with its long-stalked outer flowers opening first.

Deflexed: bent sharply downwards.

Divaricate: (adjective: divaricated) trees or shrubs with their stiff stems and branchlets spreading at a wide angle so that they become very tangled and interlaced. Usually used for certain shrubs and the juvenile stages of some trees.

Drupe: a succulent fruit with the seed enclosed in a stony or bony covering.

Emergent: trees that tower above the canopy area of a forest and are usually scattered so that they appear as individuals or groups of individuals.

Entire: mainly of leaves; refers to a continuous margin completely lacking in teeth, although hairs may be present.

Epiphyte: (adjective: epiphytic) a plant that grows or perches upon another but is not organically connected to it.

Flexuous: having a wavy or zigzag form.

Foliolate: (leaves) having a number of leaflets.

Gland: (adjective: glandular) an organ, or part of an organ, that secretes oil, resin or other liquid.

Glaucous: having a whitish or greyish appearance, but not necessarily due to a waxy or powdery bloom.

Globose: rounded or ball-shaped.

Hemiparasite: (also known as semiparasite) a parasitic plant (e.g. species of mistletoe) that is not fully dependent upon the host plant for sustenance, but carries out photosynthesis so that as well as obtaining food from its host, it also contributes to the host's well-being.

Incised: deeply and sharply, sometimes irregularly, cut.

Inflorescence: a general term for a collection of the flowering parts of a plant, or of the arrangement of the flowers.

Keel: often refers to two, lower blunt petals on the flowers of leguminous plants (e.g. *Carmichaelia*).

Kernel: the edible seed of a nut or fruit within the shell or stone.

Lanceolate: (leaves) of a narrow oval shape tapering to a point at each end.

Local: not being found over a wide area but often occurring in rather widely scattered localities.

Midrib: the main central vein of a leaf or organ.

Montane: those areas below the subalpine and alpine regions.

Nectary: a gland exuding fluid containing sugars and other compounds as a reward for the pollinators of a flower.

Nectary lines: the coloured lines on a corolla that act as a guide for pollinators to gain access to the nectary.

Oblanceolate: (leaves) long and narrow with the broadest part towards the tip.

Obovate: (leaves) inversely ovate (egg-shaped) with the broadest part towards the tip.

Opposite: particularly of leaves, a pair of organs arising at the same level on opposite sides of the stem.

Ovate: shaped like the longitudinal section of an egg, the broadest part being towards the base.

Panicle: a loose, irregularly branched inflorescence, usually with many flowers.

Pedicel: the stalk supporting a single flower in a compound inflorescence.

Pellucid: transparent or translucent (as for the dots, or oil glands, on leaves of some plants, especially those of Myrtaceae and Myrsine families).

Perfect: a flower having both male and female functional elements present.

Petiole: (adjective: petiolate) the main stalk of a leaf.

Petiolule: the diminutive term referring to the stalks of leaflets on compound leaves.

Pinnate: (a compound leaf) with the parts or segments arranged either side of an axis, or midrib, as in a feather.

Pistil: the female reproductive part of a flower.

Process: a natural appendage or outgrowth.

Pungent: mainly of leaves; terminating in a sharp, rigid point.

Raceme: (adjective: racemose) an inflorescence having several to many stalked flowers arranged along a single stem.

Receptacle: the enlarged uppermost part of the flower stalk on which the floral parts are borne.

Rhizome: an underground stem, usually spreading more or less horizontally.

Rupestral: growing on or among rocks.

Semiparasite: an alternative term for hemiparasite (see p. 11).

Senescent: growing old or characteristic of old age.

Simple: (leaves) in one piece and not being divided into leaflets such as those of a compound leaf.

Sinuate: having shallow, broad waves to its margin.

Sorus: (plural: sori) a cluster of sporangia (spore-containing structures) prominent on the fronds of most ferns.

Spike: an unbranched inflorescence on which the flowers do not have stalks and sit directly on the stem.

Standard: (or standard petal), usually the broadly obovate or almost rounded upper petal of the flowers of leguminous plants.

Stipule: one of a pair of leaf-like or scale-like appendages at the base of a petiole, sometimes joined with the stipule of the opposite leaf so that it wraps around or forms a tube around the stem. Occurs on *Coprosma* species.

Style: the long, slender extension of the ovary bearing the stigma.

Subalpine: the lower areas of the alpine zone, above the tree line but below the true alpine zone, containing herbfields, fellfields, etc.

Tepal: an individual member of the perianth (outer part) of flowers, most often on monocotyledonous plants (e.g. *Arthropodium* and *Dianella*).

Terminal: borne at the end of a stem and thus limiting its growth.

Terrestrial: plants that grow rooted into the ground.

Tomentum: a dense, more or less matted covering of soft, more or less appressed hairs.

Umbel: a cluster of individual flowers where several flower stalks arise from the same point.

Unisexual: of or relating to one sex.

Valve: any of the several parts that make up a dry, woody capsule and which generally splits open to release mature seeds.

Whorled: (an arrangement) having three or more parts or organs, at the same level, around an axis or stem.

Wing: usually the spreading side petals on the flower of a leguminous plant. They are often shorter than the standard and longer than the keel.

Repehinapapa

- Summer green.
- Narrow, grass-like leaves.

Height: 10–30 cm

Scientific Name:
Arthropodium candidum

Other Names:
Star lily, white arthropodium

While many New Zealanders are familiar with rengarenga (Arthropodium cirratum; see p. 16), not so many are familiar with its smaller relation, A. candidum or repehinapapa. Compared with rengarenga, this species is a much more modest plant to the extent that, unless it is in flower, it can be quite inconspicuous and easily overlooked, especially if growing among grasses or other grass-like plants. It is a dainty little plant that is summer green, dying down during winter to small, conical underground tubers about 15 by 18 mm. Its narrow, grassy leaves do not emerge until spring when they then have a very fresh appearance. Usually, the flat or slightly concave leaves are 10–30 cm long by about 3–10 mm wide, erect to spreading, and their undersurfaces have a slight glaucous bloom.

Frequently, repehinapapa forms small colonies, although plants often tend to be more individual. The flowering stems are very slender and may be up to 40 cm or more long. They are either simple and unbranched or they may have several branches. The individual flowers are about 10 mm in diameter and may be solitary or in unevenly aged groups of two or three. Flowering occurs during summer, usually November–January. Generally, the flowers are white but they sometimes have a faint pinkish tinge and plants that have mauvish flowers may sometimes occur. The flowers have six tepals (petals) that are bent backwards while the basal parts of its anther filaments are hairy. Its seed capsules are angular and when mature open to expose small, black seeds.

Repehinapapa occurs in both the North and South Islands from about the Coromandel Peninsula southwards. It is not uncommon on the floors of light, open forests, in scrub, on rock faces and in other shady places.

Occasionally, plants may be observed with leaves that are tinged reddish or purplish. Forms with spotted leaves have also been noted, but generally they are the lovely soft green that is so typical of the species.

As well as its Maori name of repehinapapa it is also known as star lily or white arthropodium. Arthropodium receives its name from the Greek arthron, a joint, and pod, a foot, referring to the joint in the middle of the pedicel or flower stalk. Its specific name of candidum means shining or pure white.

Rengarenga

- Clumping evergreen.
- Leaves up to 60 cm.

Height: 60 cm
Scientific Name: Arthropodium cirratum
Other Names: Renga lily, rock lily

Around coastal regions of the North Island and the northern South Island rengarenga may be a common feature of some areas. It is a most distinctive plant that will form quite large clumps up to 60 cm or more tall. In some sites it will form large colonies and is easily recognised. Its leaves are somewhat fleshy and mid- to deep green, although in some forms their upper surfaces may have a slightly glaucous bloom. The undersurfaces are always slightly glaucous. The leaf shape is lanceolate (lance-shaped) to oblanceolate (widest towards the tip). The leaves are 30–60 cm or more long by 3–10 cm wide.

During summer it produces numerous branched flowering stems that, under good conditions, may be up to a metre tall. Its numerous white flowers are 2–4 cm wide and their tepals (petals) are turned somewhat backwards. It is the centre of the flower, however, which is the most attractive part. The upper halves of the anther tails are usually purplish and are separated from the golden-yellow tips of the anthers by a narrow band of white, making the whole effect quite charming. On some forms of this species there is less colour, but the flowers lose none of their attractiveness. After flowering, the seed capsules become a prominent feature. They are up to 13 by 10 mm and eventually split open to reveal their numerous black seeds.

Rengarenga usually grows on cliffs and clay or rock banks around the shore or near the sea, and at times it grows as an understorey plant in open coastal scrub or forest. It occurs from the Three Kings Islands, around much of the North Island coast and then in the northern South Island from Whanganui Inlet, on the west coast, and Golden Bay to Marlborough Sounds and then to a little south of Kaikoura or perhaps down to Napenape in Canterbury on the east coast. It may be locally abundant but it is sometimes absent from quite long stretches of coast where it might have been expected to occur. Plants on the Three Kings Islands and along the Northland coast to about Matapouri Bay and the Poor Knights Islands are larger and more handsome than those from further south.

Arthropodium cirratum is known as rock lily from its habit of growing in rocky places, maikaka, renga lily (a shortening of 'rengarenga'), and 'reinga lily' (a corruption of 'renga' in the mistaken belief that it occurs around Cape Reinga).

Kakaha

- Leaves long and flax-like.
- Greenish, fragrant flowers; orange fruits.

Height: Large clumps up to 1.5 m

Scientific Name: *Astelia fragrans*

Other Names: Bush lily, bush flax

This is one of the native plants commonly known as bush lily or bush flax, its latter name coming from its flax-like (*Phormium*) appearance. In some forested areas it can be most conspicuous and may constitute a prominent part of the forest floor vegetation. It is easily recognised because it forms large, dense tufts or clumps up to a metre or so tall by a metre or more across, but is easily distinguished from *Phormium* by its leaves arching gracefully outwards from the centre of the plant, quite unlike most plants of *Phormium*. A further distinguishing character is that, in transverse section, its leaves are conspicuously 'M'-shaped because of the presence of two strong secondary veins or ribs about halfway between the midrib and the leaf margins.

The leaves may be up to 2 m long by 2.5–7.5 cm wide. Their upper surfaces are usually a bright to deepish green, although their colour can vary so that plants with reddish or bronze shading on them may be observed. The undersurfaces of the leaves are often a silvery green due to a thin layer of minute scales.

When kakaha flowers, its inflorescence is produced from down among the leaves and is not always very conspicuous. It has quite a large, branched panicle and each branch has numerous small, green flowers that are highly fragrant. There are separate male and female plants, and the female flowers are easily recognised because they have no anthers. Flowering usually occurs during October and November. Female plants usually display their ripe fruits from late summer to early autumn, although plants in some districts may have ripe fruits as early as December. The fruits are greedily eaten by birds and usually do not last on the plant for very long.

Astelia fragrans used to be listed under *A. nervosa* and, just to confuse the issue, the species formerly known as *A. cockaynei* is now known as *A. nervosa*. The name *Astelia* means 'wanting a stem' and is derived from the Greek, *a*, meaning without, and *stele*, a pillar. The specific name of *fragrans* refers to its fragrant flowers.

Kakaha occurs in forests, forest remnants and scrub throughout most of New Zealand from coastal and lowland areas to lower mountain forests. It grows from sea level to 900 m. The fruits of plants growing in mountain areas often do not ripen until about May.

Kowharawhara

■ Often perching.

■ Flowers yellow-
ish to pinkish
on drooping
inflorescence.

Height: About 1 m

Scientific Name:
Astelia solandri

Other Names:
Tree bush lily

Among the New Zealand species of *Astelia*, kowharawhara, or tree bush lily, is fairly distinct, firstly because it is usually epiphytic (perching on trees) or it may be rupestral (growing on rocks) and sometimes it may also be terrestrial (growing on the ground). It may be recognised by its long, drooping inflorescence that helps distinguish it from similar species. It can often be seen growing on forest trees and sometimes on the trunk of a tree fern with its long, arching leaves drooping downwards. Where it grows on coastal rocks its leaves may often be shorter and stiffer.

The leaves of kowharawhara are usually narrower than those of similar species. They also lack the close group of three prominent veins that are visible on the upper surfaces of the leaves of similar species. It is those veins that give those species' leaves their distinctive 'M' shape in cross-section. While the three lateral veins are present and easily recognisable on kowharawhara, they are usually more widely spaced. Its leaves are 1–2 m long by 2–3.5 cm wide and when mature their upper surfaces are a bright green, although when immature they tend to be silvery. Their undersurfaces are silvery because of a layer of minute scales, so tightly pressed to the leaf that they appear as a thin, silvery skin.

The inflorescence is quite drooping and its stalk may be 30 cm to 1 m in length, while the panicle (flowering part) is 15–40 cm long. Its branches are rather widely spaced and on each branch are widely spaced flowers that may be yellowish to pinkish or, especially on male plants, maroon. The fruits are about 4–5 mm in diameter and usually a translucent green to yellowish or a dull brown. Flowering can occur over quite a lengthy period from about October to about June.

Kowharawhara usually grows in wetter lowland forests throughout most of the North Island, and in the South Island mainly in western regions to about South Westland. It ranges from sea level to about 1500 m.

The specific name *solandri* is after Dr Daniel Solander, who accompanied Captain James Cook on his first voyage to New Zealand in 1768–71. It was previously listed as A. *cunninghamii*.

Kahakaha

- Perching habit; forms large bird's nest-like clumps.

- Fruits translucent yellowish to red.

Height: 50 cm–1 m

Scientific Name: *Collospermum hastatum*

Other Names: Tank lily

This is a rather unusual species, and in New Zealand forests it occupies a similar position to that of the bromeliads (plants of the pineapple family) in the Americas. It is usually very noticeable in forested areas, where it forms large bird's-nest–like clumps up in trees.

Kahakaha, also known as tank lily, occurs in lowland forests throughout the North Island, and in the South Island to about as far south as Goose Bay (just south of Kaikoura) on the eastern coast and to about Greymouth on the western coast. It is usually epiphytic on large trees but in coastal areas may also occur on rocks. Large plants that, because of storms or just sheer weight, have fallen off trees will continue to live quite happily on the ground.

Apart from its large size, one of the distinguishing features of kahakaha is the blackish bases of its yellowish-green or medium-green leaves. Unlike the astelias, its leaves are rather stiff and do not have a graceful arching habit but curve only slightly outwards. Usually, they are 60 cm to 1.7 m in length by 5–7 cm wide and sometimes they may be of a bronzy-green colour.

The inflorescence arches out from a fan of leaves, and male and female flowers are borne on separate plants. Those of the male plant are usually shorter than those of the female but, generally, the inflorescence is 20–30 cm long. The small flowers are creamy-coloured and on the female plant are followed by rounded, translucent yellowish fruits that eventually turn red.

The rather tightly clustered leaf bases form a kind of funnel that collects and holds rainwater, and at least one species of native mosquito breeds in this convenient water supply. In that respect kahakaha performs a similar function to the bromeliads of the Americas, which provide a habitat for various kinds of creatures.

The generic name of *Collospermum* refers to its ovules or seeds being embedded in moist, sticky hairs, collo, from the Greek *kola*, meaning glue, and *sperma*, meaning seeded. Its specific name of *hastatum* means spear-shaped and probably refers to the shape of its leaves.

Turutu

- Clump-forming to creeping and spreading.
- Greenish to whitish flowers in very loose spikes.

Height:
Up to 60 cm

Scientific Name:
Dianella nigra

Other Names:
Blueberry

Also known as blueberry, turutu or *Dianella nigra* is quite a common species over most of the country. It is a tufted herb growing up to about 60 cm tall, although in some areas it will grow to about 80 cm tall. Its slightly woody stems creep out from the original plant to form small colonies usually not far from the parent plant. The foliage is rather reminiscent of a miniature New Zealand flax or *Phormium*; however, its much smaller size and creeping habit usually prevents any confusion. It can be quite common on road banks in some forested or semi-forested areas.

The leaves are distinctly keeled in a similar manner to those of *Phormium* but are not rigid, and are also arranged in fans. They are 25–60 cm long by 1–1.8 cm in width, although some forms may have leaves up to a metre long by 2.5 cm wide. Leaves are slightly arching, their upper surfaces are somewhat shiny, yellowish-green and along the margins there is a broad strip of deeper green. Especially along their lower portions, the margins are rough to the touch. The leaf undersurface is dull, while the midrib is purplish.

The flowering stem is very slender, normally much-branched, and it usually overtops the leaves. The small flowers are greenish- to purplish-white, about 6–9 mm in diameter and inconspicuous. They are followed by fruits that are 6–17 mm by 6–10 mm, with each fruit borne on a very slender stalk so that the least movement causes them to tremble. The fruits also drop off the flowering stem very easily. Turutu's fruits are dull and their colour is quite variable, ranging from a rich, deep violet-blue or indigo-blue to a paler blue or a greyish-white.

Turutu occurs in open forests, on banks, along track edges and on road banks. In some areas it may be locally abundant, although sometimes it may be scarce to just locally abundant. It is distributed throughout most of the North Island as well as much of the South Island, but there are some areas such as the Canterbury Plains where it may be absent. It normally flowers in November–December and fruiting occurs in December–April.

In older books D. *nigra* was known as D. *intermedia*. *Dianella* is the diminutive of Diana, goddess of the chase after whom the genus is named. At least two other native species of *Dianella* are now recognised.

Wharariki / Mountain flax

Of the two species of New Zealand flax this is the smaller. It is rather variable both in size and in where it grows, but it can always be recognised by two characteristics. Firstly, when it flowers the three outer segments (tepals) of the flowers are always yellow to reddish-brown while the three inner segments are green or greenish-yellow. Secondly, the flowers are cylindrical in outline and not conspicuously three-angled as are those of P*hormium tenax* (p. 28). The seed pods also distinguish the two species. Those of wharariki nearly always hang downwards from the stem, whereas those of P. *tenax* always stand erect. The seed pods of wharariki are spirally twisted, something that P. *tenax* never exhibits.

The leaves of P. *cookianum* are 60 cm to 1.5 m long and 2.5–6.2 cm wide. They vary from a pale green to yellowish-green or a rather bright green. The form of the plants can vary considerably according to where they grow. Those from the higher mountain regions can be rather small with quite stiff and erect leaves no more than 60 cm long, whereas those from coastal regions may have quite long and lax leaves that droop and are up to a metre or more in length.

The colour of the flowers also varies according to region. The scape (flowering stem) can be 60 cm to 2.1 m long and the individual flowers are 2.5–4 cm long. The seed capsules may be 10–17.5 cm in length and, particularly when newly formed, they can be very ornamental. Wharariki flowers in November–January. Plants growing in coastal regions usually flower earlier than those in alpine regions. Tui and bellbirds are exceptionally fond of the watery nectar of the flowers.

Wharariki is not uncommon in scrublands, on hillsides and along streamsides from coastal to subalpine regions of the North, South and Stewart Islands. It occurs from North Cape southwards and ranges from sea level to 1370 m.

As well as sometimes using the fibre of the plant, Maori used to collect and consume the nectar.

In older books this species is listed as P. *colensoi*. The name P*hormium* comes from the Greek *phormos*, a basket or wickerwork, which was a name used by Aristotle for a plant from which mats were woven and was thus adopted as a name for New Zealand flax.

New Zealand flax / Harakeke

- Flowers dull red or reddish-brown.
- Seed pods erect.

Height: Up to 3 m

Scientific Name: *Phormium tenax*

Other Names: Flax; (flower stem) korari

Without any doubt New Zealand flax has been the most important of our native fibre plants. It provided the early Polynesian settlers with a utility fibre that had a multitude of uses. It was used for the manufacture of warm garments, cord and fishing nets, kete (baskets), paraerae (sandals), whariki (mats) and a host of other items.

New Zealand flax is also a very variable plant: it ranges from being quite tall with stiff, erect leaves to more medium-sized with drooping leaves; there are all manner of variations in between. It is distinguished from P. *cookianum* (p. 26) by its much larger size and occurs in a wide range of habitats from coastal and inland swamps to damp alluvial ground and drier hillsides. It also extends to lower mountain regions.

The leaves are 1–3 m or more in length by 5–12.5 cm in width and when mature the pointed apex of the leaf usually has a split. Leaves are yellowish-green to deep green above and their upper surfaces are rather flat, but they are quite strongly keeled beneath and often glaucous.

The flower stalk or scape (korari) is very variable in height and may be anything from 1.5 to 4.6 m tall; it is quite stout, usually a reddish-purple and sometimes glaucous. The flowers are numerous and 2.5–5 cm long. They are normally a dull red or brownish-red and are easily distinguished from those of P. *cookianum*. After flowering, the seed capsules form. They are 5–10 cm long, stout and are usually erect, three-angled and become almost black when nearly ripe. While those of P. *cookianum* almost always hang downwards and are spirally twisted, those of P. *tenax* always stand upwards and are never twisted.

New Zealand flax is abundant throughout the North, South, Stewart and Chatham Islands. It is also found on the Auckland Islands but may have been introduced there by a group of Maori inhabitants during the mid-19th century. It also occurs on Norfolk Island. The plant ranges from sea level to 1370 m.

Maori used to recognise over 60 varieties according to their uses and some were cultivated near their villages. Some were most suited for cordage, others for fishing nets and others for rain-capes. Maori used to collect and consume the thin, watery nectar of the flowers. In season, tui and bellbirds are exceptionally fond of the nectar.

■ Creeping swamp plant.

■ Flower and seed heads up to 30 cm long, brown

Height: 2–3 m

Scientific Name: *Typha orientalis*

Other Names: Bulrush

Raupo is well known to most New Zealanders. It is sometimes known as 'bulrush', a name that possibly should more correctly be applied to *Schoenoplectus tabernaemontani* (kuta). Raupo is a summer-green plant that will grow 2–3 m tall, often forming large colonies in marshy, swampy places or shallow water around lake margins. It has long, strap-shaped leaves up to about 3 cm wide that are quite spongy, particularly towards their bases. It is most easily recognised by its distinctive flower and seed heads that usually appear from about December onwards.

Raupo has creeping underwater rhizomes that are about 3–4 cm in diameter; known as korere, they taste sweet and were eaten raw by Maori, as were the young shoots of undeveloped leaves. The flower heads are more than 30 cm long and are produced on flowering stems that are usually shorter than the leaves, although that does not mean they are any less conspicuous. The male part, at the top of the head, is very narrow and spike-like, while the female, or main part of the flower head, is about 2.4 cm or so in diameter and up to 30 cm long. The female part is a lovely warm brown and persists until it matures and seeds when it becomes a darker brown.

Raupo is found throughout most of New Zealand from the Kermadec Islands, the North Island and the South Island to about as far south as the Clutha River. It does not appear to occur in Southland. Taranaki Maori apparently introduced it to the Chatham Islands in about 1832 when they invaded those islands.

To Maori, raupo was a most useful plant. Its dry leaves were incorporated in the decorative linings of their whare runanga or meeting houses; they were also used for thatching and as a bedding material. Raupo leaves were also used in poi making. It was, however, the pollen from the flower heads that was most valuable as a source of food. Large quantities of the yellow pollen (called pungapunga) were collected at the height of summer, when it was ripe. After being carefully separated, this was mixed with water, made into cakes or loaves, called pua, and then placed in an umu (oven) to bake. In some areas these cakes were likened to gingerbread.

The common name is generally spelled as 'raupo' but there are a number of (inaccurate) variations from 'rapoo' to 'raupu' and 'rapu'.

- Leaves narrow, iris-like or grassy.
- Seed pods hard yellowish (*L. ixioides*), black (*L. grandiflora*).

Height: 30–50 cm

Scientific Names:
Libertia grandiflora and *L. ixioides*

Other Names:
Common libertia; (Maori) mikoikoi, tukauki

Although we have several species of *Libertia*, there are only two that are likely to be commonly encountered around most of New Zealand. They are *L. grandiflora* (upper photo) and *L. ixioides* (lower photo). Both are commonly referred to as New Zealand iris or by their Maori names of mikoikoi or tukauki; nobody has ever bothered to distinguish one from the other because they have a very similar appearance.

Both species have green or yellowish-green foliage and they form densely tufted clumps up to 50 cm tall, with their leaves arranged in fans similar to those of a *Dianella* (p. 24). They are 30–60 cm long by 3–15 mm wide and have quite prominent midribs that are usually yellowish. The leaves of plants in open or sunny situations are usually yellowish or orange-yellow, but those on plants in shaded situations are normally green with just the midrib being yellowish.

The flowers are borne on branched stems that are fairly rigid. On *L. grandiflora* the stems are considerably longer than the leaves so that the flowers stand well clear of the foliage, whereas on *L. ixioides* the flowering stems are shorter than the leaves so that the flowers are not quite so well presented. Flowering usually occurs in October–November. The individual flowers are white, 1.5–3 cm in diameter and their tepals (petals) are wide-spreading. The three outer tepals are much larger than the three innermost ones. After flowering, rounded seed capsules form. Those of *L. grandiflora* are about 1.5 by 1 cm and when they first form are greenish but at maturity generally turn black. On *L. ixioides*, however, the capsules are up to 1.5 cm in diameter, but are often less, and at maturity their colour varies from yellow to orange. The seeds of both species are yellow or orange.

L. grandiflora occurs in the North and South Islands from North Cape to about Nelson and Marlborough. It usually grows along stream-sides and on the forest floor in lowland and hilly forests. *L. ixioides*, on the other hand, occurs in the North, South and Stewart Islands from North Cape southwards. It can be rather common along stream-banks, on rock faces or ledges, and in light open forest or scrub. It ascends from sea level to 600 m.

Libertia ixioides is also referred to as the common libertia and turutu, the latter also being the usual Maori name for *Dianella nigra*.

Easter orchid

This is one of the loveliest of our native orchids and is very easily recognised. Usually, it has a rather tufted habit, although sometimes quite large clumps of it may be seen extending for some distance along a tree branch. The Maori name for this species is raupeka, but it is most generally known as Easter orchid because it usually flowers at Easter time or thereabouts. Its generic name is derived from the Greek *earinos*, meaning vernal or spring, from the time of the year when our other native species (E. *mucronata*) usually flowers. *Earina autumnalis* was discovered by Johann Reinhold Forster at Dusky Sound in March 1773. He described it as 'spreading a very agreeable smell'.

The leaves of this orchid are produced along (often short) cane-like stems that may be more or less erect or slightly pendulous, and at other times they may even be up to a metre in length. The leaves are quite narrow, widest at their sheathing bases, and are 5–12 cm long by 5–10 mm wide. They are rather thick and tough with their upper surfaces smooth and shiny.

The flowers are the main attraction of this species. They are produced from the tips of the stems on short, branched panicles, 5–10 cm long. The white flowers of the Easter orchid have a yellow centre on the lower lip, and are 10–13 mm in diameter. Usually, there are one to four on each branch. They are deliciously scented and often when you are walking in the forest about Easter time their beautiful perfume will make its presence known well before the plant is actually observed. Flowering time is generally February–April but sometimes it may occur as late as June.

The Easter orchid is not uncommon in lowland and lower hill forests throughout most of the North, South, Stewart and Chatham Islands. Normally, it grows as an epiphyte on trees where it can be observed on branches; sometimes it may be rupestral (growing on rocks or rock outcrops), and occasionally it will grow on banks. It may also be seen on fallen trees or branches where it will survive for quite some time. The species ranges from sea level to 600 m.

Easter orchid is sometimes known as bride's bouquet, fragrant earina and sweet-scented earina.

Winika

- Narrow leaves.
- Flowers white and magenta.

Height: Stems up to 1 m

Scientific Name: *Winika cunninghamii*

Winika cunninghamii is the largest-flowered and the showiest of our native orchids. Winika is said to be the old Maori name for this species, although, strangely, it does not appear in any of the literature recording Maori plant names. The story regarding its Maori name is that Te Winika was the name given to the sacred war canoe (waka taua) of the Tainui people. Before it was felled, the totara tree that was used to make this canoe had the winika orchid growing on it and so, accordingly, the canoe was named Te Winika.

The species was formerly classed in the genus *Dendrobium*, which occurs widely through southern Asia, the Pacific and eastern Australia, but in 1978 it was considered that the sole New Zealand species, *D. cunninghamii*, did not readily fit within that genus and so it was placed in a new monotypic (having only one species) genus, namely *Winika*.

Older plants often attain very large sizes and may form very large clumps on trees. Winika can be quite noticeable with its long and slender, yellowish, cane-like stems hanging down for up to a metre or more in length. Its narrow leaves are 3–5 cm long by about 3 mm wide, deep green or occasionally yellowish and are distributed along the stems.

The flowers are produced on one- to six-flowered inflorescences that may be longer or shorter than the leaves. The individual flowers are 2–2.5 cm in diameter and are usually white with the lobes at the sides of the basal portion lower lip being partly rose-pink or more usually magenta, while the central portion at the base of the lip is greenish. Sometimes, forms on which the whole flower is more or less pinkish may be found and occasionally pure white forms may also be seen. A little-known common name for this orchid is 'lady's slipper' because of the shape of its unopened flower buds. It is also sometimes known as Christmas orchid (for the flowering time) or bamboo orchid (for the stems).

Winika occurs in the wetter lowland forests throughout the North, South and Stewart Islands, although it is absent from the drier south-eastern area of the lower North Island and much of the drier eastern area of the South Island. Usually, it grows on well-lit tree trunks and branches, but will occasionally grow on rock outcrops and cliffs. It ascends from sea level to 600 m. Flowering occurs in December–January.

- Creeping; leaves in tufts.
- Leaves harsh, rigid, very narrow, green to golden.

Height: 60–90 cm

Scientific Name:
Desmoschoenus spiralis

Other Names:
Golden sand sedge

Just as the genus W*inika* (p. 36) is monotypic (having only one species) so is pingao, another species that is confined to New Zealand. Its scientific name is derived from the Greek *desmos*, a bond, and *schoenus*, perhaps referring to its affinity with the genus *Schoenus*. It used to be quite common on sand dunes around much of our sea coast. However, it has suffered from the depredations of rabbits and hares, which are rather fond of it, even though its leaves are quite tough; habitat modification and competition from the introduced marram grass (A*mmophila arenaria*) have also greatly reduced its former abundance. In fact, it used to be one of the principal sand binders, helping to hold and protect the dunes against erosion. It is also a very important and valuable plant for Maori who used it, together with other materials, for the decorative weaving on the tukutuku panels in their more important communal buildings. It was also used for other weaving and kit (kete) making.

Pingao is a fairly stout and rigid plant, 60–90 cm tall, with thick underground rhizomes that grow through and under the sand, thus helping to hold it and fix it in place. Its leaves are produced in tufts, stiffly curved and spreading and their margins are harsh to the touch. The flower stem, up to 90 cm tall, is three-angled and very distinctive. It has a reddish-brown flower head that is usually 7–20 cm or more in length, spiral-shaped and very densely arranged, usually being composed of up to about 12 clusters of stalkless spikelets, each of which is marked by a long, leaf-like bract that extends out from its base.

Pingao occurs in the North, South, Stewart and Chatham Islands. It can be found on coastal sand dunes and while once common is now far less so. When pingao grows on a sand dune, it helps to create a gently sloping dune that is aerodynamically far more resistant to damage from strong winds than those dunes that are covered with marram grass. Marram grass creates a fairly steep-sided dune that is much more prone to wind damage; storms in particular will carve out large gaps in the dune, which then becomes prone to further damage. The native spinifex grass (kowhangatara) that occurs in the North Island and eastern parts of the South Island also creates aerodynamic dunes that are said to be more resistant to wind erosion.

Pepepe

- Large, clumping plant.
- Leaves flat, bright green, iris-like.

Height: 1 m

Scientific Name: *Machaerina sinclairii*

Other Names: (Maori) toetoe tuhara, tuhara

Pepepe is a very easily recognised plant that belongs to the sedge family. It forms bold clumps 50 cm to 1 m tall with bright green, iris-like leaves. The leaves are 30 cm to 1.5 m long, quite flat, of a tough texture but not rigid and have a lax habit. They are smooth and shiny; a distinguishing character useful for identification is a broad, shallow notch where the leaf margin meets its sheathing base.

The rather rigid flowering stems are 50 cm to a metre or more in length. They are topped with a flowering panicle that is 15–40 cm long. It is much-branched and drooping and has numerous spikelets of a rich reddish-brown. The nuts or seeds are small and 2–2.5 mm long.

Pepepe occurs in the North Island from North Cape southwards to Hawke's Bay, Taupo and the Whanganui River; it then extends further south to the Kaimanawa, Ruahine and Tararua mountain ranges. It is not uncommon on damp or wet rock faces, stony cliffs, papa clay cliffs and road banks. In some areas, particularly those such as along the Whanganui River, great clumps of it may be seen adorning the cliff-like river-banks. The species ranges from sea level to 450 m.

Pepepe is also known by other Maori names, toetoe tuhara and tuhara, while one author has unimaginatively referred to it as the broad-leaved sedge. The species was first observed by Joseph Banks and Daniel Solander, who accompanied Captain James Cook on his first voyage to New Zealand during 1768–71.

Toetoe

- **Large clump-forming grass.**
- **Plume-like flower heads.**

Height: 1.5–2.5 m

Scientific Names:
Cortaderia richardii,
C. toetoe

Other Names:
(Maori) toetoe
kakaho, kakaho
(flower plume)

Commonly known as toetoe, at least five native species of this genus exist in New Zealand. They are our largest native grasses and may be seen in most parts of the country, where they are sometimes a conspicuous feature. Unfortunately, two introduced species of *Cortaderia* (the pampas grasses *C. selloana* and *C. jubata*), from South America, have become widely naturalised and constitute serious plant pests.

The Maori name of toetoe is quite commonly misspelt and mispronounced as 'toitoi'. Variations of its Maori name are toetoe kakaho, toetoe makoro and toetoe rakau. The flowering plumes are referred to as kakaho.

The easiest way to identify the native species of toetoe is to examine the leaf sheaths at the base of the leaf, where they wrap around each other. The sheaths have a white, waxy bloom (absent in the pampas grasses) and conspicuous nerves or veins between the midribs and the leaf margins. In addition, the old, dead leaf sheaths of the native species do not curl into a spiral as do the old sheaths of the pampas grasses. Generally, too, the native species are earlier flowering than the pampas grasses, although that is by no means universal.

The various species of toetoe grow 1.5–2.5 m tall and form large tussocks or clumps. Their leaves have roughened margins that are quite sharp and are capable of inflicting painful cuts. Their flowering stems may rise to 3–6 m tall and when they first flower they have very handsome and showy flower plumes that are usually a buff to yellowish colour. Flowering of the native species usually occurs in November–December, although one North Island species may flower as late as January–February. Toetoe was used medicinally by Maori for at least one internal ailment and the plumes were used as a poultice for burns.

The various species are quite adaptable and may be seen growing in swamps, on sand dunes, in bush clearings, along stream-banks and in coastal areas. Their range extends from the sea coast to 1100 m. *Cortaderia toetoe* is confined to the lower North Island while *C. richardii* is found only in the South and Stewart Islands. Of the three remaining species, *C. fulvida* occurs in the North Island and the very north of the South Island, *C. splendens* is confined to the upper North Island, and *C. turbaria* occurs only on the Chatham Islands.

- **Usually a bushy shrub.**
- **Leaves oval, reddish blotches.**

Height: 2–3 m

Scientific Name: *Pseudowintera colorata*

Other Names: Pepper tree, red horopito

Horopito is one of our most distinctive and easily recognised native shrubs. It is also the more common of the two better-known *Pseudowintera* species. Generally, it is quite distinctive, with the upper surfaces of its leaves being yellowish-green to yellowish-brown and usually heavily blotched with reddish colours, while their undersurfaces are whitish-green to glaucous. A related species, *P. axillaris*, has green leaves and is never marked with reddish blotches.

While *P. colorata* is mostly seen as a much-branched shrub up to about 2–3 m tall, it will occasionally make a small tree. The rather shortly stalked leaves are 2–8 cm long by 1–3 cm wide and they vary in shape from elliptic to broadly elliptic or broadly obovate (widest towards the tip) and they have blunt tips. Flowers are produced in clusters of two to five in the leaf axils. They are yellowish to yellow-green and rather saucer-shaped to almost flat. Flowering can occur from August till March, depending upon habitat and regional circumstances. The flowers are followed by reddish or black, berry-like fruits that are 3–4 mm long, produced at any time between December and June.

Horopito is mainly a plant of forest margins and second-growth scrub, and when growing in such well-lit situations its leaves become very strongly marked with red. In some South Island mountain areas the leaves can be completely red and very handsome. It is one of the few shrubs that deer and other browsing animals normally leave untouched. When the leaves of *P. colorata* are chewed they are very pungent, with a hot peppery taste.

Maori used a decoction of the leaves as a stimulant and for stomach-ache, while the sap was used for the treatment of skin diseases and venereal diseases. The masticated leaves were also used to relieve toothache and by Maori women when they wished to wean their babies; the juice of the masticated leaves being rubbed onto the nipples of their breasts to give them a bitter taste. The early European settlers used it as an astringent and occasionally its bark was used as a substitute for quinine.

P. colorata can be common in lowland to high mountain forests in the North Island from north of Auckland southwards. It is common throughout most of the South Island as well as on Stewart Island. It occurs from sea level to 1200 m.

Leafless clematis

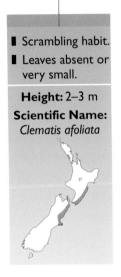

- Scrambling habit.
- Leaves absent or very small.

Height: 2–3 m

Scientific Name: *Clematis afoliata*

Among the species of native *Clematis* the leafless clematis is unique. When not in flower it resembles nothing more than a tangle of leafless, yellowish-green, rush-like stems draped or sprawling over a convenient shrub or rocks. As such, it attracts very little attention; however, when it flowers, during October or November, it is quite transformed and becomes a thing of rare beauty. It is then a mass of yellowish flowers with a slight greenish tinge (they may be likened to chartreuse), but its perfume also scents the surrounding air for quite some distance, especially on warm spring mornings when there is just a gentle north-west wind. The scent is reminiscent of the Australian *Boronia megastigma*.

Especially in some of the South Island's mountain river valleys, its stems often present a very distinctive appearance because they lie in the direction of the prevailing wind. The leafless clematis is a scrambling rather than a climbing plant because although it will scramble up through the branches of some shrub, the stems do not twine around the shrub for support.

Clematis afoliata is a much-branched shrub with leafless, wiry stems and branchlets. The only time that it may have a few leaves is during the spring when it is making active growth and a few vestigial leaves will appear on the young branchlets. Alternatively, if part of the plant is growing in heavy shade it may also produce a few leaves on that shaded part. In spite of not producing leaves, it still produces leaf stalks that may be straight or spirally coiled. These tendril-like leaf stalks are capable of tightly coiling around the branchlets of its supporting shrub so that the clematis branchlets will not be dislodged by strong winds. Flowers are produced in clusters of two to five; they usually have four tepals (petals) and are 6–7 cm in diameter. Male and female flowers are on separate plants and, after flowering, the female plants may be identified when they flaunt their silvery, silky-plumed seed heads.

Leafless clematis occurs on the east of the North Island from Hawke's Bay south to the Wairarapa and the southern Wellington coast, while in the South Island it is confined to Marlborough and the northern part of Canterbury. It has reportedly been recorded from the Waitaki Valley and Otago. It usually occurs in rocky and open places and open scrubland in the dry eastern areas of both islands. The species is found from sea level to 760 m.

Clematis foetida / C. cunninghamii

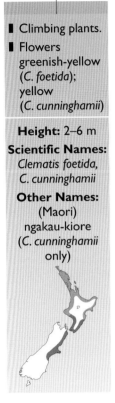

- Climbing plants.
- Flowers greenish-yellow (C. foetida); yellow (C. cunninghamii)

Height: 2–6 m

Scientific Names:
Clematis foetida, C. cunninghamii

Other Names:
(Maori)
ngakau-kiore
(C. cunninghamii only)

Clematis foetida (upper photo) occurs in the North and South Islands, and it is quite similar to C. cunninghamii (lower photo), which occurs only in the North Island. While C. cunninghamii has several Maori names, ngakau-kiore being one of the more usual ones, C. foetida appears to have no common name. Its specific name of foetida means bad smelling, which is unfortunate because its yellow-green flowers are quite sweetly scented. It is only when you experience the perfume in large amounts that it can be quite overpowering and, to some individuals, may be regarded as offensive. Older plants, in full bloom, will literally smother themselves with flowers. Flowering occurs during September–November.

C. foetida can be a stout, woody vine and on old plants its main stems may be up to 6 cm in diameter; it will ascend to 6 m or more. Its dark green leaves are three-foliolate with the leaflets 2.5–5.7 cm long by 2–3.7 cm wide. Their margins may be entire to wavy to slightly lobed. Flowers are produced in branched panicles that arise from the leaf axils; those of the male plant are up to 2.5 cm wide with five to eight tepals (petals) while the female flowers are slightly smaller.

C. foetida occurs in scrub in open places and around the margins of lowland forests throughout the North and South Islands from about the Wanganui area to Peel Forest in South Canterbury. It was first discovered near Akaroa, on Banks Peninsula, sometime between 1840 and 1843 and is still common on the hillsides above the town.

C. cunninghamii (formerly known as C. parviflora) is distinguished from C. foetida by its smaller size and more slender habit, usually growing to only about 3–4 m, as well as by its smaller and thinner leaves. Its leaves are three-foliolate, the leaflets 1–4 cm long with entire margins or some toothing or lobing. The flowering panicles do not have as many flowers as those of C. foetida and its small, yellowish flowers have narrow tepals (petals) and are not as intensely coloured as that species. Sometimes it is more noticeable after flowering, when its silvery, plumose seed heads adorn some forest plant. It occurs from the Three Kings Islands through the North Island to about Wanganui and Waipukurau but can be rather local in its occurrence. Flowering is in September–November. It was discovered near Whangaroa, in 1826, by the botanist Allan Cunningham.

Puawhananga

- Tall climber; leathery leaves.
- Large, white flowers.

Height: 3–6 m

Scientific Name:
Clematis paniculata

Other Names:
(Maori)
puawananga

Puawhananga is surely the best-known and most beautiful of our native climbing plants and, in the spring, its lovely white flowers may be seen adorning trees in many forest areas. It is a vigorous climber that will ascend to considerable heights up forest trees, but it may also be seen adorning lower scrubby vegetation along forest margins.

On old plants the main stems of this species may grow to as much as 10 cm in diameter and it may ascend to 10–12 m or even higher. Its leaves are on tendril-like stalks up to 4–5 cm long and they have rather stout leaflets that are 5–10 cm long by 2.5–5 cm wide. The leaflets have a leathery texture, their upper surfaces being dark green and shiny while the undersurfaces are paler. Puawhananga produces numerous flowers usually in August–November, and then the forest really comes to life with numerous splashes of its pure white flowers.

Puawhananga commences life as a small seedling on the forest floor with leaves that bear little resemblance to those of the adult, but once it commences to climb its leaves gradually change until they assume the thick and leathery nature of the mature plant.

Its Maori name of puawhananga or puawananga has been translated, correctly or incorrectly, as meaning 'sacred flower'. According to ethnologist Elsdon Best, the Urewera Maori considered that puawhananga was one of the first-born children of Rehua (the star Antares) and Puanga (the star Rigel in Orion). Its duty was to indicate, by means of its blossoms, the coming warmth of spring. The first Europeans to record puawhananga were the father and son, Johann Reinhold Forster and Johann Georg Forster, who in 1773 accompanied Captain James Cook on his second voyage to New Zealand. They discovered it in Queen Charlotte Sound.

Puawhananga is common in lowland and lower montane forests from the Three Kings Islands south throughout the North, South and Stewart Islands. It is found from sea level to 760 m.

C. *paniculata* was introduced into cultivation in England as early as 1840. One plant growing under glass, in Massachusetts, USA, was estimated to have had 7000 flowers open at one time.

Peperomia urvilleana

New Zealand has two native species of *Peperomia*, the more common being *P. urvilleana*; the second species, *P. tetraphylla*, occurs only in a limited area of the North Island. *Peperomia* is a large genus of over 1000 mainly tropical and subtropical plants, being found particularly in South and Central America. *Peperomia urvilleana* has the distinction of being the southernmost species of the genus.

It is a herb, growing to 10–30 cm tall, and may be recognised by its light green, fleshy stems, along which are distributed rounded leaves. The leaves are quite succulent, and are usually a light to medium green, with shiny upper surfaces. They have very short stalks, are alternate and 1–4 by 1–2 cm with blunt tips. The slender flower spikes are quite erect, growing usually from near the tips of the branchlets, and are up to 2.5 cm long and on stalks about 1.5 cm long. The seeds are very small, green or blackish, and they are distributed all along and around the spike. They are slightly sticky so that when touched they will stick to the skin.

Peperomia urvilleana occurs from the Kermadec Islands, throughout the lowland North Island and in the South Island in scattered localities from Pelorus Sound and Golden Bay to Westport and finally reaching its southern limit at Punakaiki on the west coast. It frequently grows in rocky places, in light forest, while in coastal and lowland regions it may be rupestral (growing on rock). Another favourite habitat is fallen tree trunks or branches, on which it grows as a low epiphyte. In some situations it grows on coastal rocks no more than 2 m above high-water mark where it may be splashed by the salt spray. Flowers and fruits may occur during most of the year.

Peperomia is derived from the Greek, *peperi*, pepper, and *homoios*, resembling, alluding to the fact that the plants resemble and are closely related to true pepper (*Piper*). Its specific name of *urvilleana* commemorates the French navigator and naturalist Dumont d'Urville (1790–1842).

Kawakawa

- Blackish stems.
- Minute flowers on greenish spikes.

Height: 2 m

Scientific Name: *Macropiper excelsum*

Macropiper excelsum, or kawakawa as it is generally known, is sometimes referred to as pepper tree but it should not be confused with horopito (*Pseudowintera*), which is also referred to as pepper tree.

Kawakawa has broadly heart-shaped leaves and its blackish stems have conspicuously swollen joints so that it is easily recognised. It grows as a shrub about 2.4 m tall or occasionally into a small tree up to 6 m tall. The leaves are opposite, about 5–10 cm long by 5.7–11.2 cm wide; they are broadly rounded with a short drawn-out tip and are heart-shaped at their bases. They are deep green if growing in the forest but may be yellowish-green when growing in more open situations. In the wild the leaves are usually quite severely holed due to the depredations of native insects, usually the kawakawa looper caterpillar; in fact, it is rare to come across a kawakawa whose leaves are not full of holes.

The individual flowers are produced on greenish, erect spikes that are 2.5–7.5 cm long. These flowers are quite minute and very closely placed around the spike. After pollination the flowers gradually swell and become fleshy to form small, berry-like fruits that are yellow to bright orange.

Kawakawa occurs in coastal forests and scrublands throughout the North Island and in the South Island to Banks Peninsula on the east coast and to Okarito on the west coast. It also occurs on the Chatham Islands. The species has aromatic leaves and bears some resemblance to the kavakava of the Pacific islands, hence its Maori name of kawakawa. The fruits were eaten, although mainly by children, and, when ripe, were said to have a luscious flavour.

Kawakawa was much valued by Maori who had about 30 uses for it, mainly of a medicinal nature. It was used as a diuretic, to allay toothache, for easing stomach pains and in the treatment of gonorrhoea. The leaves and bark were used to treat wounds and cuts, while hot liquid made from boiling the leaves was used in the treatment of severe bruising, and a similar infusion was employed to prevent swelling after an injury. Although its similarity to the kavakava of the Pacific islands has been noted, the roots appear to have little or none of the properties that would have made it suitable for preparing a drink similar to that of the intoxicating kavakava.

Porcupine bush

- Rounded, stiff-branched shrub.
- Small leaves; appears leafless.

Height:
60–70 cm

Scientific Name:
Melicytus alpinus

This unusual and distinctive shrub receives its common name because the spine-like tips of its young branchlets give it a rather porcupine-like appearance. *Melicytus alpinus*, along with several other native trees and shrubs including mahoe, is a member of the Violaceae (violet family).

As a wild plant it is often a flattened, sprawling shrub against rocks or, if in more open situations, a hemispherical shrub, 60–70 cm high, with very tightly interlaced branchlets. An unusual character is that its young branchlets are spine-like and appear as though they are there to protect the shrub against the depredations of browsing animals. While they are quite rigid, their tips are actually blunt and would offer scant protection in this regard. There is a theory that such shrubs, of similar divaricating form, evolved as a response to the browsing of the now extinct moa. However, because this shrub frequently grows in rather harsh and exposed situations the spine-like tips of its young branchlets would appear to be an adaptation largely to protect it against the desiccating effects of alpine winds.

The bark is greyish and the leaves occur mainly inside the bush. They are alternate and often produced in small clusters; each leaf is 1–1.2 cm long by 1.5–3 mm wide and widest towards its blunt tip, and its upper surface is deep green. The numerous small flowers may be seen on the plant during spring and are borne on the mature stems inside the bush. They are whitish, about 3 mm in diameter and their petals are quite strongly curved outwards. The fruits are berry-like, about 4 mm in diameter and when ripe during late summer are white, flecked and blotched with very dark purple. Generally, they tend to be well hidden inside the shrub and to view them it may be necessary to part some of the branches.

The porcupine bush is mainly a South Island species, but it does occur in the southern North Island in the Wairarapa area. In the South Island it occurs east of the Southern Alps in fellfields and rocky places in montane to subalpine regions, especially in Marlborough and Canterbury, but it also occurs in the drier parts of Nelson. Some closely related forms occur in Otago and northern Southland, but their status has yet to be determined.

Melicytus novae-zelandiae

- Sprawling or erect, bushy shrub.
- Shiny green leaves, margins toothed.

Height: 3 m

Scientific Name:
Melicytus novae-zelandiae

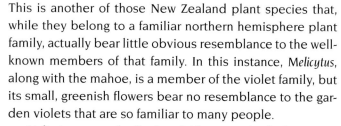

This is another of those New Zealand plant species that, while they belong to a familiar northern hemisphere plant family, actually bear little obvious resemblance to the well-known members of that family. In this instance, *Melicytus*, along with the mahoe, is a member of the violet family, but its small, greenish flowers bear no resemblance to the garden violets that are so familiar to many people.

Melicytus novae-zelandiae is a fairly stout shrub that grows up to 3 m tall, or it may be quite a straggling shrub. It has rather broadly rounded, blunt-tipped leaves that tend to be leathery. The leaves are on short stalks and are 4–6.5 cm long by 2–3.5 cm wide, their margins are coarsely but distantly toothed and a pattern of netted veins is distinct on their upper surface, while on their undersurfaces a network of very fine veins is quite obvious.

The small, greenish flowers are 3–4 mm in diameter and bell-shaped, with the tips of the petals turned and rolled outwards. The sepals are pale green or mid-purple in colour. Flowering usually occurs August–September and the male and female flowers arise on separate plants. After flowering, the berries form; when mature they are about 7 mm long and are white shaded and spotted with very dark purple. They are usually on the plant from August to October.

Melicytus novae-zelandiae occurs on the Three Kings Islands and then southwards in the North Island to about the Bay of Plenty. It is found mainly on coastal islands and it has been observed that plants growing on offshore islands such as the Poor Knights generally have much larger foliage than those on or close to the mainland. A similar or closely related species occurs on Kapiti Island as well as on the outer and western islands of the Marlborough Sounds.

Melicytus novae-zelandiae was first discovered on the Cavalli Islands, in 1834, by the botanist Richard Cunningham, who travelled from Australia in 1833 to follow the journey made earlier by his brother Allan. While on that expedition he also collected many plant specimens.

Although an attractive plant, *Melicytus novae-zelandiae* has never had a Maori name recorded for it, and it has certainly never warranted sufficient attention from New Zealand's Pakeha settlers to have had a European common name bestowed upon it.

Horokaka

- Trailing plant.
- Thick, succulent leaves.

Height:
Trailing

Scientific Name:
Disphyma australe

Other Names:
Pig's face,
native ice plant

Horokaka is one of the few truly succulent herbs that occur in the New Zealand flora. While its older stems may be semi-woody, its three-sided or three-angled, succulent leaves are thick and fleshy.

It has a prostrate or trailing habit. The stems may be up to a metre or more in length, although, depending on where the plant grows, they may be much shorter. Its leaves are opposite or in opposite clusters, they are joined at their bases and are 2–4 cm long by 4–6 mm wide; their tips are either somewhat pointed or rather bluntish. When in flower horokaka is quite noticeable with its many-petalled pink or white flowers, 2–4 cm wide. Its urn-shaped seed capsules are fleshy and have a flattish top that, when ripe, has several slits which open to release its seeds. Flowering is usually from spring to mid- or late summer.

Horokaka is common around coastal regions of the North and South Islands as well as on Stewart Island and it usually grows on banks, rocks and cliffs. It also grows on clay cliffs and on some gravelly areas. The species is absent from some areas of the western and southern South Island coast.

A related species, D. *papillatum*, occurs on the Chatham Islands. It differs in usually having more brightly coloured flowers and in its leaves having roughened surfaces instead of being smooth as are those of D. *australe*.

Horokaka is also known as pig's face, native ice plant, Maori ice plant, New Zealand ice plant, ruerueke and ngarangara. Around some parts of the coast it has hybridised with the introduced South African ice plant or hottentot fig (*Carpobrotus edulis*), which is so common on many of our sandy beaches.

Maori used to squeeze out the juice from the succulent leaves of horokaka, and they applied it to boils and abscesses in order to encourage the drawing out of pus and to alleviate inflammation. The juice was also used as a treatment for itch (waihakihaki).

New Zealand spinach / Kokihi

- **Trailing or sprawling.**
- **Leaves diamond-shaped, fleshy.**

Height:
Low–growing, 10–15 cm

Scientific Names:
Tetragonia tetragonioides (New Zealand spinach); *T. implexicoma* (beach spinach)

In New Zealand there are two species that are commonly known as New Zealand spinach, although strictly speaking only one of those (*Tetragonia tetragonioides*) qualifies for that appellation; T. *implexicoma* (pictured; formerly known as T. *trigyna*) should more correctly be known as 'beach spinach'. Both species have the Maori name of kokihi.

Tetragonia tetragonioides is a decumbent (low-growing) herb with branching stems that are softly woody towards their bases and may spread 60 cm or more. Its stalked leaves are diamond-shaped to triangular; they have blunt tips and their upper surfaces are generally densely papillose (covered with small, soft protuberances). The small, yellowish flowers are solitary or in pairs and are followed by hard, angled, two- to four-horned seed capsules that are usually top-shaped. Unlike those of T. *implexicoma*, the seed capsules of T. *tetragonioides* are not distinctly red-coloured.

On his second voyage to New Zealand (1772–75), Captain Cook was reputed to have gathered T. *tetragonioides* along with several other species of plants that were used as an antiscorbutic (to prevent scurvy); however, it appears that Maori did not much use this plant for culinary purposes.

Kokihi occurs on coastal sands, dunes and stony beaches in the Kermadec Islands and around the North, South and Stewart Islands. It is now rather rare in the wild. Although known as New Zealand spinach, it also occurs in Tasmania, Australia, the Pacific Islands, Japan and southern South America. On the other hand, the beach spinach or kokihi (T. *implexicoma*) is much more common as a wild plant, being found on coastal sands, dunes and rocky places on the Kermadec, Three Kings, North, South, Stewart and Chatham Islands.

Depending upon where it is growing, kokihi may have a scrambling or semi-climbing habit as it grows through and over low, shrubby vegetation. Beach spinach often has reddish stems and its leaves are often slightly smaller than those of T. *tetragonioides*, which are triangular to broadly diamond-shaped and with blunt tips. The yellow flowers are solitary or paired. Its seed capsules are not horned and are usually a bright to dark red. While its leaves are edible it is not often eaten and, because of its oxalic acid content, should be consumed only in small quantities. The same applies to T. *tetragonioides*.

Shrubby tororaro

For those who are familiar with the climbing and scrambling species of *Muehlenbeckia*, which are ubiquitous in many parts of the country, M. *astonii* is completely anomalous because it is so distinct from the other species. Known as shrubby tororaro, for want of any other common name, M. *astonii* is a shrubby plant that grows 1.2–2 m tall.

As might be expected with a *Muehlenbeckia*, it is usually much-branched with the branches often being very interlaced (divaricating), and its zigzagging branchlets are slender and flexuous, with dark reddish-brown bark. Its very small leaves are usually produced in clusters of two or three on short side branchlets. The leaves are 7–8 mm in diameter, heart-shaped and slightly notched at their tips; their upper surfaces usually bright green and their undersurfaces paler. During the winter the bush is leafless, but once spring arrives the fresh green leaves soon appear.

Shrubby tororaro flowers in December–January and its tiny flowers are in small clusters less than 1 cm wide. As with the other species of *Muehlenbeckia*, its fruits consist of the succulent, white or translucent swollen remains (the tepals) of the flower with a small black, three-angled nut sitting in the centre. Sometimes the fruit is dry and not succulent.

Shrubby tororaro is a comparatively rare plant and is regarded as endangered, although it is more widely distributed than might be supposed. In the southern North Island it occurs in the southern Wairarapa and on the shores of Cook Strait from Honeycomb Light to Sinclair Head, and in the South Island it is found along the eastern coast of Marlborough, from Seddon to the Waima River, and then down to Canterbury where it occurs at Birdlings Flat, at the south-western edge of Banks Peninsula, and finally on Kaitorete Spit, east of Lake Ellesmere, its southernmost limit. It usually grows in coastal to lowland areas in open shrubland on river terraces, stony ground and open rocky hillsides.

The name tororaro more correctly refers to M. *complexa* (p. 68) a usually scrubby semi-scrambling species that occurs in open situations, scrublands and coastal areas of the three main islands. The name shrubby tororaro has been coined to distinguish this species from M. *complexa*. The genus *Muehlenbeckia* commemorates a Swiss botanist and physician, H.G. Muehlenbeck (1798–1845). The specific name *astonii* commemorates B.C. Aston, a New Zealand botanist.

Black vine

- Vigorous, smothering climber.

- Fruits whitish, translucent.

Height: 3–10 m

Scientific Name: *Muehlenbeckia australis*

Other Names: Pohuehue (erroneous); (Maori) puka

Muehlenbeckia australis is usually a rampant vine that often grows so vigorously that it can almost completely smother all growth on other trees and shrubs. Especially in some districts and particularly in the southern portion of the South Island, it can frequently be quite a problem. Its common name of black vine has been used in various districts around the country since at least as early as 1911 and, apart from the little-used Maori name of puka (recorded by William Colenso, Richard Cunningham and Henry Williams), there does not appear to be any other recognised Maori name for it. As not infrequently happens, well-meaning but ill-advised authors have taken the Maori name of M. *complexa* (pohuehue) and applied it to M. *australis*, with the result that the name has stuck. In fact, there is no evidence that Maori ever used pohuehue as a name for this species.

Black vine will grow to 10 m or more and covers shrubs or small trees, and it will also trail over rocks. It appears to be more prevalent around forest margins and where the original growth has been disturbed and scrubby growth has regenerated. In old forest, black vine's smothering tendencies do not appear to be nearly so noticeable because its top growth is usually confined to the tops of the larger trees.

The upper surfaces of its ovate to heart-shaped leaves are dark green and on adult plants they are 2–8 cm long by 1–3 cm wide with slightly undulating margins. The leaf shapes can be variable, especially on younger plants, and they may range from being lobed to fiddle-shaped. The small greenish flowers are produced in panicles up to 15 cm long, usually from the tips of the branchlets. After flowering, its fruits may be dry or succulent with the old flower parts enlarging to become translucent and succulent with a glossy, black seed sitting in its centre. Flowering and fruiting may take place in November–April.

Muehlenbeckia australis occurs throughout New Zealand from the Three Kings Islands south throughout the North, South and Stewart Islands. It is common in lowland to montane areas and is found in forests, around forest margins and in scrublands. It also occurs on Norfolk Island. Its specific name of *australis* means southern and does not refer to Australia as might be thought.

Pohuehue

Apart from M*uehlenbeckia australis* (p. 66), this species is probably the most common of the native species of M*uehlenbeckia*, being found throughout all main islands of New Zealand and in a great variety of habitats. It is a somewhat variable species but mostly it forms dense and hummocky masses that can be very springy and have earned it a variety of common names. Apart from its Maori name of pohuehue, it has been known to Maori as tororaro, but to Pakeha it is known as mattress plant, which is self-evident to those who are familiar with it. Wiggy-bush (dating from as early as 1934) is another common name that conjures up visions of its twisted and twiggy appearance; and yet another name is black vine, which is used principally in the Taihape and central North Island areas as well as in Westland. It should be noted that black vine is also used as a common name for M. *australis* (p. 66). There are also several other common names for M. *complexa* that are now seldom used and probably better ignored.

Pohuehue has slender stems that either creep or twine around some other support and, for want of that support, it will climb upon itself. Its slender stems are usually tightly interlaced, reddish-brown and quite wiry. Its often rather sparse leaves are on slender stalks up to 1 cm long and the leaf blade is 5 mm to 20 cm long by 2–15 mm wide. The shape of the leaves on the one plant may be quite diverse while their margins may be lobed or entire. The flowers are borne on short spikes, about 2 cm long, which arise from the leaf axils and the tips of the branchlets. One little-known fact about pohuehue is that its flowers are deliciously scented. As with the other M*uehlenbeckia* species, the old flower parts enlarge to become succulent and translucent with a shiny, black, three-angled seed sitting in the centre. Although the fruits are small and rather tasteless, Maori children apparently used to collect and eat them raw.

Pohuehue occurs in coastal, lowland and montane areas of the North, South and Stewart Islands where it is found in open and rocky places and forest margins. It not infrequently grows around the margins of tidal estuaries and inlets, often in company with the shore ribbonwood (*Plagianthus divaricatus*). It also occurs on Lord Howe Island.

Glasswort

Glasswort is a very common species that may form extensive colonies in salt marsh and estuarine areas, and sometimes on coastal rock platforms. It is an apparently leafless, succulent plant with greenish, greyish-green or reddish stems and may form individual patches up to 60 cm or more in diameter. The basal parts of its stems are prostrate and woody, but all of the upper portions are usually erect, quite soft and succulent. Its stems are of quite variable length and in some situations may be up to 30 cm long, but mostly they are shorter and more in the order of 7–10 cm long.

At one stage *Sarcocornia* was considered to be leafless, but it was later discovered that what were believed to be segments of the stem were, in reality, the fleshy internodes or leaf bases. The stems are completely covered with pairs of leaves that are fused together to form a rounded collar or joint with two minute lobes. These leaves are translucent, succulent and green or flushed with red.

The small flowers are produced from the leaf axils on the upper portions of the branchlets and they form a spike with shorter, thicker joints. The flowers are sunk into the axils, usually about five to ten per ring. The fruit of the glasswort is more or less ovoid with small seeds about 2 mm in diameter. Flowering generally occurs throughout summer and autumn.

Glasswort is found in the North and South Islands and on the Chatham Islands.

It is not generally known that the fleshy stems of the glasswort are edible and may be used in salads. They taste a little salty and have an unusual flavour that is not unpleasant but difficult to define. The generic name of this plant, *Sarcocornia*, comes from the Greek *sarx* or *sarkos*, meaning fleshy, and *cornea* meaning horny, while its specific name of *quinqueflora* means with five flowers, and refers to the ring of flowers around the stem. In Europe the common name of the European glasswort (*Salicornia fruticosa*) arose because the ashes resulting from when it was burnt were referred to as berilla and were used for the manufacture of soap, as well as glass, hence its name of glasswort. Our native species was formerly known as *Salicornia australis*.

Gunnera prorepens

Most people are familiar with the giant South American species of *Gunnera* (*G. tinctoria* and *G. manicata*) that commonly feature around ornamental ponds; they are jocularly referred to as giant rhubarb, but many would be unfamiliar with their diminutive New Zealand relations. In fact, the former species *G. tinctoria*, from Chile, has now become a serious pest, particularly around parts of the North Island west coast, especially around the Taranaki area. While South America has the giants of the genus, all of the New Zealand species are just the opposite and are quite small. Of the native species, *Gunnera prorepens* is quite distinct and easily recognised and is unlikely to be confused with any other New Zealand species of *Gunnera*.

It is a prostrate, usually wide-spreading creeping plant that will form patches of variable size according to the growing conditions. Its numerous leaves are either erect to spreading; they are tufted at the nodes or joints of the stem and do not form distinct rosettes. Its thin leaf blades may be 3–6 cm long by 1–4 cm wide and more or less oval in shape. Their upper surfaces brownish to purplish-green and their entire margins may have obscure, rounded teeth or be obscurely sinuate (broadly wavy).

The flowering stems may be up to 6 cm long and they stand erect from among the leaves. Male and female flowers are on separate plants. The female flowers are quite close set and, after pollination, the rather short flowering stem lengthens. The flowers are followed by bright red, top-shaped fruits about 3–4 mm long. It flowers in spring or early summer and the fruits generally ripen during March–April.

Gunnera prorepens occurs in the North, South and Stewart Islands, in damp or boggy places from Auckland southwards, in lowland to lower subalpine regions. It is found in herbfields, grassland or damp places in the forest and is often seen creeping through sphagnum moss. The species occurs from sea level to 1100 m.

One author has referred to it as the creeping gunnera, but, as all of the native gunneras have a creeping habit, such a name is of little use. No suitable common name for it has originated. The genus *Gunnera* is named in honour of Johan Ernst Gunnerus (1718–1773), a Norwegian bishop and botanist. Its specific name, *prorepens*, means creeping.

Taranga

- Erect shrub.
- Bright green leaves.

Height: 2 m

Scientific Name:
Pimelea longifolia

The genus *Pimelea* is mainly confined to New Zealand and Australia, but there are a few species on Timor and Lord Howe Island. *Pimelea longifolia* was the first species discovered and was collected at Tolaga Bay, in 1769, by Joseph Banks and Daniel Solander during Captain James Cook's first voyage to New Zealand. Later, in 1773, during Cook's second voyage, the Forsters, father and son botanists, Johann Reinhold and Johann Georg, were able to collect several additional species of *Pimelea* from various localities.

Taranga is an attractive shrub that can be variable in habit: plants growing around the Auckland area are often 2 m tall, while those in other localities such as the lower North Island may be much smaller and no more than low-growing or trailing shrubs, while those of the South Island are often bushy shrubs up to about 60 cm tall. As is common among the *Pimelea* species, they have very tough inner bark and consequently their stems are not easily broken.

The bright green leaves are broadly lance-shaped and 2.5–7.5 cm long by 8–20 mm wide. The leaf has a pointed tip and a very short stalk so that it appears to sit directly on the branch. The inflorescences are compact heads borne at the tips of branchlets and composed of numerous flowers. These vary from white to pale pink and are usually sweetly scented. There are three kinds of flowers: perfect (or hermaphrodite), all male, or all female. The perfect flowers have stamens and carpels, and so are capable of producing seeds, while those flowers that are only male or female are capable of fulfilling only one function, so that the all-female flowers need to receive pollen from an all-male plant or a hermaphrodite plant. Flowering usually occurs September–January. Unlike some species of *Pimelea* that have succulent fruits, taranga produces its seeds as a dry fruit that is covered with silky hairs.

Pimelea longifolia occurs in the North and South Islands from about Doubtless Bay, in Northland, southwards. In the South Island it is found from Pelorus Sound to north-western Nelson and then southwards to near the southern end of the Paparoa Range close to Greymouth. It grows in lowland to montane scrublands and open places but is rather local or absent from some South Island areas. The species ranges from sea level to 900 m.

Wharewhareatua

Of the 26 or so native species of *Pittosporum* all are trees or shrubs that grow terrestrially (in the ground), with the exception of two species that are epiphytic, more usually growing as epiphytes perched up in trees, on rocks or only occasionally as ground-growing shrubs.

Wharewhareatua is a small, more or less erect shrub that may grow to about 2 m tall but is usually less. Its leaves are 3.5–7.5 cm long by 1.5–3.5 cm broad; they are ovate to diamond-shaped, pointed, and produced in whorls of three to five around the branchlets. Their upper surfaces are deep green and shiny and the undersurfaces are paler. Flowering may commence as early as June in the far north or not until September further south.

The flowers are produced in branched clusters from the tips of the branches and branchlets and, unlike many other *Pittosporum*, its flowers have a rather spidery appearance. Their narrow, pointed petals are a light pinkish-red to yellowish and they are slightly recurved. Often the male and female flowers are on separate plants, or some hermaphrodite flowers may also be present. The seed capsules are about 1.5 cm in diameter, and the most remarkable thing about them is that they split open to reveal the insides of the two or three bright orange capsule segments with a cluster of black seeds in the centre.

While wharewhareatua is mainly epiphytic on trees, or sometimes on rocks, it is probably most commonly found growing intermixed with other epiphytes on large forest trees, particularly with *Collospermum hastatum* (kahakaha, p. 22) or *Astelia solandri* (kowharawhara, p. 20) and especially on a large rata (*Metrosideros robusta*). It occurs in the North and South Islands from near North Cape southwards and is common in the Auckland region, but is said to be more common on the eastern side of the North Island. In the South Island it is found from Marlborough Sounds and north-west Nelson, especially West Wanganui Inlet, southwards to about Greymouth in Westland. Usually, it occurs in lowland and lower montane forest from sea level to about 600 m.

The specific name of *P. cornifolium* is derived from the supposed resemblance of the leaves of this species to the cornel or dogwood (*Cornus*), hence the Latin *cornus*, cornel or dogwood, and *folium*, a leaf.

Pittosporum divaricatum

- Erect shrub.
- Densely twiggy with blackish stems.

Height:
2–3 m

Scientific Name:
Pittosporum divaricatum

Many New Zealanders are familiar with the common species of *Pittosporum* such as kohuhu (P. *tenuifolium*) and lemonwood or tarata (P. *eugenioides*), but few are aware that there are several small shrubby species that, at first glance, appear to be most unlike a *Pittosporum*. It is only when their flowers and seed capsules are closely examined that their affinities can be recognised. There are about seven of these divaricating species of *Pittosporum* that collectively are such a feature of New Zealand's flora; plus two others that, at some stage in their development, go through a divaricating phase.

One such species, in particular, is P. *divaricatum*, which is a rigid, rather erect shrub up to 2 m or possibly 3 m tall and has a densely divaricating habit. Its bark is very dark, while that of its branchlets is a dark reddish-brown, so that the whole bush has quite a dark appearance. Young plants actually go through a juvenile phase that, to a casual glance, does not appear to be very different from that of the adult.

In this juvenile phase the very small, linear leaves, usually about 10–12 by 1–2 mm, are often irregularly lobed around their margins. In common with the adult foliage their upper surfaces are a deep green, which further enhances the dark appearance of the bush. In its adult phase the leaves are still somewhat variable, with margins that are only shallowly lobed or entire (not lobed). Juvenile and adult leaves are often intermixed on the bush.

The small, very dark reddish flowers are borne singly and, because of that, they do not make a very noticeable display. The pointed tips of their petals roll backwards and outwards while the bases of the flowers are slightly inflated. The seed capsules of P. *divaricatum* are globose and about 5–8 mm long. They are green at first, but as they mature they become almost black with a rather granulated outer surface. When ripe their two sections split open to reveal two to six black seeds. Flowering is usually about October–November and fruiting from about January onwards.

Pittosporum divaricatum is found in the North Island from about the Volcanic Plateau southwards and in the South Island mainly east of the Southern Alps. It occurs principally in upper montane forest (mainly beech forest) and in sub-alpine scrub from near sea level to 1000 m.

- Tall forest climber.
- Bright carmine flowers.

Height:
to 15 m

Scientific Name:
Metrosideros carminea

The genus *Metrosideros* occurs in New Zealand and Australia, and then from Polynesia to Malaysia, but it is only in New Zealand that the climbing species are found. In this country we have six climbing species of rata, as they are commonly termed. One or two of them are very beautiful plants that delight travellers in bush areas with their flowers. *Metrosideros carminea* or akakura is one of the most beautiful, but, unfortunately, it is apparently not now nearly as common as in former times; fortunately, it is common in cultivation. Possibly forest clearance and the introduced possum are responsible for its decline in the wild.

Akakura is quite a tall and sturdy climbing plant. In common with the other climbing species of rata it clings to the host tree by means of short aerial roots. A young plant that is still actively climbing its support usually has quite small, rounded, opposite leaves, while its stems cling tightly to its host tree. Once it attains maturity, it commences to branch outwards and become bushier. It is on these branching growths that its flowers are produced.

The leathery adult leaves are broad, deep green and shiny, more or less pointed at their tips and on such short stalks that they appear to have no stalks at all. They are 1.5–3.5 cm long by 7–10 mm wide. A careful examination of their undersurfaces will reveal that there are minute oil glands present but that they are not particularly noticeable. The bright carmine flowers are produced in terminal clusters from the tips of short branchlets. While the flowers have small coloured petals that tend to soon fall, it is really the carmine filaments of the stamens that provide the flowers with all of their brilliance. Flowering usually occurs during September–October but it may occur as early as August in favoured districts.

Akakura is confined to lowland forests of the North Island where it is found from North Cape to Auckland and South Auckland then to the Coromandel Peninsula, the Kaimai Range, Great Barrier Island and Great Mercury Island. It is more plentiful in Northland, although it is now regarded as being an endangered species. The prefix 'aka' was used by Maori to describe any climbing plant, hence its common name of akakura.

- **Tall climber or scrambler.**
- **Orange to orange-red flowers.**

Height: 10 m

Scientific Name: *Metrosideros fulgens*

Other Names: (Maori) akatawhiwhi; scarlet rata vine

With its displays of bright orange or orange-scarlet flowers, this species is the most flamboyant of the climbing species of rata, except for M. *carminea* (p. 80). It usually flowers between late summer and mid-winter, after the other species of climbing rata have finished flowering. Its specific name of *fulgens*, from the Latin *fulgere*, means shining or glistening, and is possibly in reference to its vivid display of flowers, although it could also refer to the leaves.

Aka is a fairly tall liane, climbing up trees to 10 m or more. Its quite thick main stems, up to 10 cm in diameter, have a distinctive appearance as they are covered with bark that peels or flakes off in fairly large pieces. Its thin, young stems attach themselves to the host plant with small aerial roots after the fashion of an ivy plant. If there is not a convenient tree for it to climb, aka will sprawl over the ground to form dense thickets or tangles.

The opposite leaves are rather large, being 3–6 cm long by 1–2.5 cm wide; they have a thick texture, their upper surfaces are shiny but not glossy and their tips are blunt. It is when aka flowers that it really displays its true glory. The orange or orange-red flowers are produced from the tips of the branchlets in clusters that have few or many flowers. Its brightly coloured staminal filaments are 2–2.5 cm long. Flowering usually occurs in February–June, producing brightly coloured splashes that enliven the forest scene. In most years it is possible to observe it flowering at odd times through the autumn and winter. Occasionally, yellow-flowered forms of this species occur. Its woody seed capsules are urn-shaped and are almost enclosed within the ovary of the flower, a feature that does not occur in any other species of rata.

Metrosideros fulgens grows in coastal and lowland forests on the Three Kings Islands, in the North Island and in the northern South Island from northern Marlborough, including the Marlborough Sounds, through to Nelson and then west of the Southern Alps in Westland to about as far south as Martins Bay.

As well as being known as aka or akakura, this species has various other common names, including akatawhiwhi, akatorotoro, kahikahika and scarlet rata vine. In 1857 one enterprising author was so impressed with its thick stems that he even referred to it as the 'vegetable boa constrictor'.

Akatorotoro

Metrosideros perforata is in some ways quite similar to M. *diffusa* (not described here) but it can be distinguished and recognised by the fact that its leaves have numerous distinct little oil glands on their undersides. While this character is present on the leaves of other species of climbing rata, it is not nearly as obvious as it is on the leaves of M. *perforata*.

Akatorotoro is quite a high-climbing species and will ascend to 15 m or so on tall trees. When a young plant first begins to climb, its leaves and all of its growth cling tightly to its support, the small aerial roots being attached to its host very much after the fashion of ivy. These young leaves are quite closely placed on the stem and are almost rounded. Once the plant reaches maturity the leaves gradually change, becoming more broadly oval with bluntish tips, rather leathery in texture and with margins slightly recurved. The adult leaves are about 6–12 by 5–9 mm with deep green and somewhat shiny upper surfaces.

The flowers are generally white, although pinkish forms do occur. Unlike M. *diffusa*, a similar species that produces its flowers from the old stems, on M. *perforata* they are produced towards the apexes of the branchlets. There are usually about three flowers in each cluster and each flower is around 15 mm in diameter. Flowering may occur from mid- to late summer, usually from January. Its smallish seed capsules are rounded, 3–5 mm in diameter, and when ripe their tops split into three openings.

Akatorotoro occurs on the Three Kings Islands, throughout the North Island and in the South Island to as far south as Martins Bay on the west coast and Banks Peninsula on the east coast. It grows in coastal and lowland forests, on rock and rock faces, around forest margins and on cleared areas where it often grows as a densely bushy shrub up to 1–1.5 m tall. In some districts where the forest has been cleared these shrubby rata bushes can be quite a feature of the vegetation. As the vine ages its stems often become detached from the supporting tree and hang free from some high branch. Such free-hanging stems may be of considerable thickness; up to 15 cm would not be uncommon.

Akatorotoro has at least 13 other common names, including box rata, climbing rata, koro and whakapiopio.

Hibiscus diversifolius

- Shrubby; lobed leaves.
- Large flowers, pale lemon, with maroon blotch.

Height: 2 m

Scientific Name: *Hibiscus diversifolius*

While doubt has sometimes been cast on the authenticity of the indigenous status of this Hibiscus, which some authorities consider to be an introduced plant, a pollen record from a 2000-year-old peat core, obtained from the Mt Wellington area of Auckland, may possibly belong to this species, thus indicating that H. *diversifolius* could well be indigenous.

Depending on where it grows, this species is a stout, softly woody shrub or a perennial, the stems of which are woody towards their bases. It will grow to 2 m or more tall and varies in its habit from being a flat and trailing plant to one that is quite erect. The stems usually have sharp prickles. Its leaves are on stalks up to 8 cm long and measure 5–14 by 3–13 cm. They are three- to five-lobed, and are rough to the touch because of numerous small projections on their surfaces.

The flowers are quite spectacular, being up to 8 cm or more in diameter. They are produced from the tips of the branchlets and are a pale lemon-yellow, while inside around the centre there is a maroon or dark purplish-brown blotch. The flowers of this species and H. *trionum* (p. 88) remain open for only one day before they gradually wither. The seed capsules are prickly with sharp hairs and measure about 2 by 2 cm; after opening they can remain on the bush for quite long periods.

Hibiscus diversifolius occurs in the North Island from North Cape to about Hokianga in the west and the Bay of Islands in the east. It grows in sandy coastal places, in raupo swamps, on slow-flowing stream-sides and in coastal scrub, where plants are never far from the shoreline.

Because it is frost tender, there are only limited habitats where it can grow and there are only about 12 wild populations in existence. It is easily destroyed by browsing farm livestock as well as goats and wild pigs. Consequently, it is now a seriously threatened plant. At North Cape there is a prostrate form that grows on the serpentine rock of that area, but elsewhere it is usually erect. *Hibiscus diversifolius* is also native to eastern Australia, Norfolk Island and some other Pacific islands. The specific name *diversifolius* refers to the diverse nature of the shapes of its leaves.

- **Erect to spreading stems.**
- **Flowers creamy-yellow.**

Height:
40–60 cm

Scientific Name:
Hibiscus trionum

Hibiscus trionum, like *H. diversifolius* (p. 86), is a species whose indigenous status has been called into question. Because it is so rare in the wild, being mainly confined to only about five localities, some authorities consider that it may be an introduced species.

Puarangi is a herb, usually up to 40–60 cm tall, but in favourable localities it can grow to about twice that height. Initially, it sends up an erect central stem, but subsequent stems grow out sideways, more or less horizontally, before becoming upright at their tips to eventually become erect. The stems are coarsely hairy, and the rather variable leaves are on stalks about 0.5–1 cm long. The leaf blades are smooth and hairless, three- to five-lobed and are of two kinds. The basal leaves are broad, more or less 7 by 5 cm and coarsely toothed or lobed around their margins, while those on the upper parts of the stem are narrowly divided into three to five segments with the terminal segment being about 8 by 2.5 cm, and coarsely toothed around their margins.

The flowers are up to about 8 cm in diameter, pale lemon-yellow to almost creamy-yellow, and there are two forms. The most commonly known form has a very dark, blackish-maroon blotch around the bases of its petals (main photo). On the backs of the petals, where they are partially exposed in the bud, they are somewhat flushed with a reddish-purple. A second, less commonly known form has a slightly smaller flower, without the maroon blotch (inset photo). The seed capsules are surrounded by the papery calyx segments, which give them an inflated appearance. When they ripen, the pods turn blackish and they contain numerous black seeds, about 2–3 mm in diameter. The flowers of this species and *H. diversifolius* remain open for only one day before they gradually wither.

Puarangi is found in only a few localities, mainly on the Northland peninsula but also on Great Barrier Island, Mayor Island and at Hicks Bay. The form with the maroon blotch in the flower occurs at Spirits Bay, near Cape Reinga, and one or two other localities, while the smaller-flowered form, without the blotch, occurs at the nearby Tom Bowling Bay and also on Mayor Island. While most authorities state that puarangi is an annual or biennial plant, it is actually a perennial. It has also featured on one of our postage stamps. Puarangi is the Maori name used in the Te Kao district of Northland.

Waiu-atua

■ Spreading, forming colonies.

■ Reddish stems, narrow grey leaves.

Height:
40–60 + cm

Scientific Name:
Euphorbia glauca

This, our sole native species of *Euphorbia*, is an interesting plant. It is strange that of the 2000-odd species of *Euphorbia* worldwide, only one is native to New Zealand.

Waiu-atua is an attractive plant with its greyish or glaucous leaves contrasting most effectively with its reddish stems. It normally grows to a height of 40–60 cm, although occasionally it may be taller. It is a rhizomatous herb that spreads by its underground rhizomes and can form quite large colonies. The erect stems at first are greenish, but their upper portions become reddish with age. Narrow leaves are mainly crowded along the upper portion of the stem and are about 2–10 cm by 1.5–2.5 cm. They do not have a leaf stalk and their bases clasp around the stem.

The flowers are produced from the tips of the stems in umbels, which means that their flower stalks (usually five) are all of a similar length and they arise from a common base. Sometimes these primary flower stalks are branched. The flower stalks are clad with leaves that are shorter and broader than the stem leaves. What might be taken for the flowers are technically referred to as glands or nectaries. They are surrounded by deep-reddish, cup-shaped structures with reddish-purple glands in their centres, and they have crescent-shaped horns. It is these glands that add considerably to the attractiveness of this plant. Its seeds are pale yellow or purplish-brown.

While once regarded as common, waiu-atua is now a rather uncommon species with a declining habitat. Even though it occurs in the North and South Islands, and on Stewart Island as well as on the Chatham Islands, it mostly grows in only scattered localities. The South Island localities where it may be seen include on the coastal rocks at Punakaiki in Westland, and also at Dummies Beach in Southland. Fiordland is a stronghold for it. It is found in coastal localities, on sands, gravels and in rocky areas.

Bush lawyer (*Rubus australis*)

■ Tall forest climber.

■ Stems, leaves with prickles.

Height: To 10 m

Scientific Name: *Rubus australis*

Other Names: (Maori) tataramoa, taramoa

Of the five native species of *Rubus*, four are known as bush lawyer, or often simply as 'lawyer'. With their hooked prickles they can be fearsome plants that will soon entangle the unwary and inflict painful scratches. Contrary to what most New Zealanders may think, the term 'lawyer' is not a local term but is derived from the old Kentish (England) dialect. It was used to describe the long, trailing vine of a bramble, which could readily ensnare people. The term was soon added to the New Zealand vocabulary when the term 'bush' was conjoined with it. It is used to refer to a plant that is difficult to escape from, once entangled in it. A 'bush lawyer' signifies an unqualified person who has no formal qualifications in law but professes to be knowledgeable about it, often to the detriment of the person who is unfortunate enough to attract that person's attention.

Rubus australis is a common species that is recognised by the undersurfaces of its leaves being smooth and hairless while their three to five leaflets are rounded and more or less broadly ovate, and its fruits are yellow-orange. It is a high-climbing species with stems up to 10 m or more long, although more often than not it is likely to be seen climbing through marginal vegetation. It is frequently seen scrambling over the forest floor before it commences to climb some handy support. Its stems, leaf stalks and the midribs along the backs of its leaflets are armed with backward-facing prickles which enable it to climb trees or shrubs. The leaf stalks are about 2–5 cm long and the leaflets are on stalks up to 5 cm long.

The white flowers are borne on branched or unbranched inflorescences, and the male and female flowers are produced on separate plants. The yellow-orange fruits are about 9 mm long and resemble a small raspberry. Flowering occurs in September–November while fruiting may be in October–February.

Rubus australis occurs in lowland to montane forests in the North, South and Stewart Islands. In the South Island it is more common on the western side of the island. It is also known by its Maori names of taramoa, tataramoa and tataraheke. Up until 1961 there was confusion over the various species of *Rubus* and this species was misidentified as what is now known to be R. *cissoides* (p. 94).

Bush lawyer (*Rubus cissoides*)

This species of 'lawyer' is much more vigorous than the preceding (*Rubus australis*, p. 92) and may have stems up to 15 m or more long, while, with age, its main stems can be very stout and may be up to 10 cm thick. Possibly, it is this character that earned it the name of Captain Cook's ropes, which was apparently used in the Otago region in the late 19th century. In addition, it was known to Maori as tataramoa, which literally means 'to hold the moa'. Obviously, the moa-hunter Maori considered that once a moa became entangled in the stems of the bush lawyer it would be unlikely to escape or, at least, not before they had a chance to dispatch it.

Rubus cissoides is a rather variable species and some North Island forms of it are quite distinct from those commonly seen in the South Island. Usually, it has three to five leaflets, although commonly there may be only three. On North Island plants the leaflets are generally 7–15 cm long by 3–10 mm wide, but on some plants they may be no more than 1.5–2 cm wide. The leaflets of South Island plants are generally much broader and are up to 10 cm long by 4.5 cm wide. As with R. *australis* (p. 92), the leaf stalks and midribs along the backs of the leaflets are armed with stout, reddish prickles that present a fearsome defence against those unwary enough to approach too closely. These hooked prickles enable it to climb tall trees simply by hooking into their rough bark. A young stem of this species was once observed to be about 4 m up the trunk of a tall kahikatea and gave every indication that, barring mishaps, it would eventually gain the crown of the tree where it would be able to branch out.

The white flowers of R. *cissoides* are produced in large panicles up to 60 cm long (inset photo). As with the other species of *Rubus*, the male and female flowers are on separate plants. Generally, flowering may occur in September–November while fruiting may be in November–April. The fruits are orange to reddish-orange (main photo).

Rubus cissoides is found on the Three Kings Islands, in the North and South Islands and on Stewart Island in lowland to montane forests. The species is so named because it resembles a genus of climbing plants, *Cissus*, which was named from the Greek *kissos*, ivy.

Bush lawyer (*Rubus schmidelioides*)

Rubus schmidelioides is distinguished from the other *Rubus* species by the undersides of its leaflets having a matted covering of fine hairs, especially when they are young. Usually, that covering gives them a slightly glaucous or whitish appearance, while their upper surfaces are a deep green. It is not such a high climber as other bush lawyers, usually reaching around 3 m or more, sometimes forming densely interwoven masses that may completely smother its supporting host.

The branchlets and leaf stalks of the leaves are heavily armed with numerous hooked, reddish-brown prickles. Generally, its leaves have only three leaflets or, rarely, five. The leaflets are somewhat variable in shape, being more or less oval; their margins are bluntly toothed, and they are often slightly convex when viewed from above. The flower panicles are shorter than those of R. *cissoides* (p. 94), being about 10 cm long, and flowering usually occurs in September–November. Its fruits are yellowish-orange and normally are on the plant during October–February.

Rubus schmidelioides occurs in the North Island and in northwest Nelson where it grows in lowland forests, ascending to about 1000 m. The specific name is derived from its resemblance to *Schmidelia*, a plant named after the 18th-century German botanist Casimir Schmidel.

In the South Island there grows what used to be a variety, named R. *schmidelioides* var. *subpauperatus* (inset photo), which is now believed to be an unnamed species. The name *subpauperatus* means impoverished, referring to the smaller size of its leaves. This particular bush lawyer has very narrow leaflets that are 5–7 cm by 6–15 mm and deep green, and lack the matted covering of fine hairs that typify R. *schmidelioides*. It has more compact flower panicles and its flowers are a greenish-white rather than white. Its fruits are yellowish.

Generally, this plant may be seen commonly in scrubby areas and forest margins where it tends to scramble through and over shrubs, often forming dense, smothering masses. It is heavily armed with hooked prickles and is guaranteed to leave any intruder into its domain badly scratched. This species occurs east of the Southern Alps in the South Island and on Stewart Island.

Leafless lawyer

Of the native species of bush lawyer, this is the most unusual. Often it is nearly or completely leafless. Apart from having no leaflets, it is easily recognised by its bright yellow prickles, and is further distinguished by its petioles and leaflet stalks. Normally, there are only ever three leaflets (rarely it may have five leaflets), while the deep green leaflet stalks are usually quite long; those of the two lateral leaflets diverge from the central stalk almost at right angles, and as they become tangled they can present a dense mass.

Rubus squarrosus has either no leaflets at all or, depending upon where it is growing, just a few vestigial leaflets at the tips of the leaflet stalks, or sometimes leaflets of normal size. If it grows in a relatively shady situation it may exhibit a reasonable number of normal-sized leaflets but, if growing in a sunny or exposed situation, mostly it will have no leaflets or the vestiges of just a few leaflets. The leaflets, when present, may be up to 10 cm long by 3 cm wide. Their upper surfaces are deep green and smooth while, unlike on the other species of *Rubus*, the midribs on their undersurfaces are completely unarmed. It is mainly the petioles and leaflet stalks that have yellow prickles, which are almost straight and not really hooked as with the other species of *Rubus*.

The flower panicles are up to 20 cm long, the slightly yellowish or creamy male flowers being up to 13 mm wide and the smaller female flowers only about 6 mm. The male flowers also have slightly pointed petals. Flowering generally occurs in September–November. It is not often seen in fruit, but its orange fruits are about 7 mm long (lower photo). Fruiting occurs in November–April.

Leafless lawyer occurs in the North and South Islands where it grows in lowland forests, usually around forest margins and in open, scrubby and rocky places. In the South Island it appears to be most common along the drier areas east of the Southern Alps. This lawyer often forms immense tangles of growth and, while it may grow in scrubby forest and does not have the opportunity to climb to great heights, it can certainly spread over quite wide areas. Because of its dense tangles the species would have most certainly been one of the plants Maori referred to as tataramoa, or capable of 'holding a moa' in its tangles.

Native broom

■ Erect shrub,
stem tips yellow.

■ White flowers
flushed purplish.

Height: 2 m

Scientific Name:
*Carmichaelia
petriei*

Other Names:
Desert broom

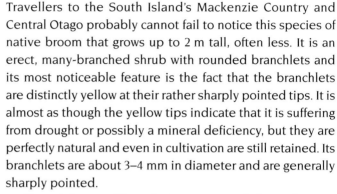

Travellers to the South Island's Mackenzie Country and Central Otago probably cannot fail to notice this species of native broom that grows up to 2 m tall, often less. It is an erect, many-branched shrub with rounded branchlets and its most noticeable feature is the fact that the branchlets are distinctly yellow at their rather sharply pointed tips. It is almost as though the yellow tips indicate that it is suffering from drought or possibly a mineral deficiency, but they are perfectly natural and even in cultivation are still retained. Its branchlets are about 3–4 mm in diameter and are generally sharply pointed.

Except for seedling plants or parts of those that are shaded, it seldom has leaves, its green stems taking their place and carrying out the plant's photosynthesising functions. In the drier parts of the Mackenzie Country and Central Otago the stems of this species are usually a greenish-yellow, while in areas that are not normally as dry they tend to be more greenish.

The inflorescences are produced from small notches on the stems, usually as one to three short racemes per notch. Its white flowers are flushed purplish with purple veining on the keel and measure about 6 by 5 mm. Flowering usually occurs in November–December. The seed pods are about 8–10 mm long and dark brown to almost black. The small seeds are usually greenish-yellow and are sometimes heavily mottled with black.

Carmichaelia petriei, sometimes known as desert broom, occurs from coastal lowland areas to montane grasslands, east of the Southern Alps, from the Mackenzie Country in South Canterbury to Central Otago and then to about central Southland. Generally, it is found in dry grassland habitats, but in some areas it may occur in moister areas along stream-sides and around forest margins. It also grows on rock outcrops and cliffs.

Sometimes it is browsed by farm stock such as cattle and sheep, and hares can also have a considerable effect on the shrub.

Prostrate kowhai

Most New Zealanders are very familiar with the common kowhai and regard it with a great deal of affection; fewer know of *Sophora prostrata*, the so-called dwarf kowhai. Its common name of prostrate kowhai is actually quite misleading because very rarely does it ever have a prostrate habit, although in some exposed localities it can be quite dwarf.

Mostly, it forms a densely interlaced shrub up to 2 m or more in height but on exposed hilltops it can grow as a hummock-shaped shrub, probably no more than 40–50 cm high, the branches of which are so tightly divaricating and interlaced that it is possible to stand on it without making any impression. The prostrate kowhai has stiff, divaricating branches with orange-brown to greyish bark and a tendency to zigzag. Compared with the other species of kowhai, its leaves are very small, being about 1.5 cm long by about 7–8 mm wide, and have upper surfaces of a very dark green. They have up to eight pairs of small leaflets plus a terminal leaflet, each more or less oval and about 3–4 mm long.

The flowers of prostrate kowhai are its most noticeable feature, even though they are considerably smaller than those of the common kowhai. They are about 2 cm long, being either solitary, in pairs or three together, and are two-toned: the standard and wings being orange while the keel is a dull yellow or greenish-yellow. Curiously, the flower stalk is quite sharply bent so that the flowers appear to be held in an upside-down position. It flowers in October–November. During the flowering season it is a great favourite of bellbirds, which carry out most of the pollination of its flowers. The seed pods are up to 7 cm long and they are not winged and angular, as are those of the commonly known S. *microphylla* and S. *tetraptera*, but are gently constricted just below each seed so that they have a smoother outline. Also, they are covered with fine velvety hairs. Normally, the seed pods contain from one to five seeds.

Prostrate kowhai occurs east of the Southern Alps, in lowland to montane areas from southern Marlborough (the Awatere Valley and Waima River) to South Canterbury and North Otago. Frequently, it grows in grassland and rocky places, but it also occurs as a component of scrubby areas in some river and stream valleys. In some areas, such as near Rotheram in North Canterbury, pure stands of it can be found.

Parataniwha

- Spreading herbaceous plant.
- Brownish-green to bronzy-green leaves.

Height:
60 cm to 2 m

Scientific Name:
Elatostema rugosum

Other Names:
Native begonia

This handsome member of the nettle family is confined to the North Island. It is a herbaceous plant that grows to about a metre tall or, in some deep, sheltered gullies, to as much as 2 m tall. It can form large colonies or thickets and is easily recognised by its soft, succulent nature. The stems are either erect or slightly arching and on large plants may be as thick as a finger.

The leaves of parataniwha are spread along most of the stem and project out along either side; at first glance they appear to be opposite but are actually alternate. They have no leaf stalks and are 8–25 cm long by 2.5–7 cm wide, slightly wider towards their tips; they are more or less unequal-sided at their bases. The upper surfaces of the leaves are rough to the touch because of small stiff hairs, while their margins are sharply and coarsely toothed. Even in quite dense shade the leaves are brownish-green to bronzy-green; with age they become lighter with darker veining, while the young leaves produce the best colour, being a bronze-green to a reddish-green. This combination of foliage colours is most attractive. The flowers are produced in small, domed heads, about 2 cm in diameter, each head comprising numerous little flowers. The flower heads may be either unisexual or mixed.

The species occurs throughout most of the North Island from North Cape to the Tararua Range. It is especially common in the northern half of the island but is local to the south of the Waikato River. It grows in lowland and hill forests, particularly along damp or wet, shaded stream-sides, banks and ravines. In some areas, such as North Taranaki, it will clothe the sides of steep, gutter-like ravines with stems up to 2 m or more tall, almost to the exclusion of all other vegetation. It is also capable of thriving in very low-light conditions.

Parataniwha is also known by the Maori name of parataniwhaniwha, and various authors have referred to as native begonia, New Zealand begonia and wrinkled elatostema, this last example being nothing more than its scientific name partially translated into English.

Ongaonga / Tree nettle

- Spreading shrub.
- Stems, leaves with white stinging hairs.

Height:
2–3 m

Scientific Name:
Urtica ferox

This shrub has a fearsome appearance and is regarded as one of New Zealand's most dangerous plants, because of the large stinging hairs that cover most of its parts. They can inflict a severe and painful sting, the effects of which may last for three or four days, or even longer, on those unwary enough to come into contact with it.

Ongaonga is a much-branched shrub up to 2–3 m tall. Its leaves, leaf stalks and young stems are protected by rigid, white stinging hairs that may be up to about 6 mm long; they are the most conspicuous feature of the plant. They are particularly numerous along the leaf veins, margins and leaf stalks. The leaves are narrowly triangular, 8–12 cm long by 3–5 cm wide. Their margins are sharply toothed and each tooth is tipped with a stinging hair or bristle. Along each side of the midrib of the leaf, the stinging hairs stand erect and present a formidable defence. Male and female flowers are on separate plants and they are produced from the leaf axils, in branched spikes up to 8 cm long. The globular, greenish flowers are quite small, usually no more than about 1–1.5 mm long. It should be noted that the flower spikes also bear stinging hairs.

Ongaonga occurs in the North and South Islands from north of Kaitaia to Wellington and in the South Island east of the Southern Alps southwards to about Otago. It can be common in coastal and lowland forest, particularly around forest margins and in shrublands. Often it can be rather dominant in forest that has been heavily degraded and opened up by stock such as cattle, goats and sheep.

Ongaonga is not a plant to be trifled with, and, in the past, it has been known to have killed both horses and dogs after they have been badly stung by it. There is also the well-known case when, in 1961, there was a human fatality, the only recorded instance. Even to this day, because of the ensuing publicity some people regard the species with almost a degree of hysteria. However, our native tree nettle should be treated with all due respect and a considerable degree of caution.

Common mistletoe

- Hemiparasite on trees.
- Oval, thick, deep green leaves.

Height: 90 cm

Scientific Name: *Ileostylus micranthus*

Other Names: (Maori) pirinoa, pirita

As its vernacular name implies, this is a very common species of mistletoe and it is a hemiparasite on quite a wide range of host plants including *Coprosma*, *Melicope*, manuka, totara, *Lophomyrtus* and various exotic trees such as tree lucerne, hawthorn, apple trees, rose and pine.

It is easily recognised by its almost broadly oval, thick, leathery leaves, which are opposite, often a yellowish-green to rather deep green and usually 2–8 cm long by 1–4.5 cm wide. Its very small, greenish-yellow flowers are produced in groups of about 10, on panicles that arise from the leaf axils. Flowering usually occurs during September–December, with fruiting in December–April. Its berries are about 5–8 mm long and bright yellow when ripe; they are soon eaten by birds and their flesh is quite sticky.

Little is known about the dispersal of native mistletoe seeds, but it may be similar to that of some overseas mistletoes. Birds eat the fruits and within a very short space of time (it can be as little as 15 minutes) the seed passes through the bird's alimentary canal before being deposited on a branch where it may then have a chance to germinate. The seeds of all mistletoes are covered by a sticky pulp so that they will readily adhere to wherever they are deposited. Occasionally, birds will place seeds on a twig or branch when they try to wipe their beaks free of the sticky pulp that contains the seed.

After the seed has been deposited and stuck on a tree twig or branch, it sits until the following spring. By then the sticky pulp will have dried out and resembles a coat of varnish, through which a small green speck shows at its larger end. Some time elapses before the next stage occurs, but at first no feeding stems appear; however, once all of the starch in the seed has been used up, long thin branches commence to grow along the branch of the host plant and down onto its trunk. If those stems touch one another they will grow together. At intervals those stems send haustoria (suckers) into the tree and at those points woolly lumps occur. They are covered with brown scales and, at the same time, the mistletoe's stems give off leafy branches so that new clumps are formed.

This mistletoe is common throughout the North, South and Stewart Islands where, as well as occurring in native forests, it may be seen on isolated native trees and a wide range of exotic trees.

Scarlet-flowered mistletoe

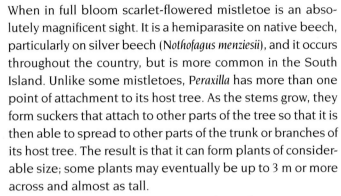

- Hemiparasite, mainly on silver beech.
- Tubular, bright scarlet flowers.

Height:
To 2.5 m

Scientific Name:
Peraxilla colensoi

Other Names:
(Maori) korukoru, pirita

When in full bloom scarlet-flowered mistletoe is an absolutely magnificent sight. It is a hemiparasite on native beech, particularly on silver beech (*Nothofagus menziesii*), and it occurs throughout the country, but is more common in the South Island. Unlike some mistletoes, *Peraxilla* has more than one point of attachment to its host tree. As the stems grow, they form suckers that attach to other parts of the tree so that it is then able to spread to other parts of the trunk or branches of its host tree. The result is that it can form plants of considerable size; some plants may eventually be up to 3 m or more across and almost as tall.

The leaves are more or less oval, 4–6 by 3–4 cm, very thick and leathery, and they are produced in pairs, each pair lying at around 90 degrees to its neighbours. The very attractive flowers are produced in groups of five to ten on short stalks, but more often it appears that there are only ever two or three flowers in a group. In bud the individual scarlet flowers are 3.5–5 cm long and, while their yellowish bases are broader than their tips, the tips are still slightly swollen and bulbous.

When the nectar-laden flowers are about to open, tui and bellbirds (which appear to be the main pollinators) seize the yellow portion of the bud with their beaks and give it a twist, which causes the four petals of the flower to burst open and coil backwards like a spring. The pollen explodes out over the bird, which then goes on to pollinate another flower. Flowering occurs in November–February, but generally in early January. The small oval fruits are about 8 mm long and yellow when ripe. As with the flowers, the fruits are eagerly sought by birds, which then disperse them with their seeds onto other trees. Mistletoe fruits ripen in December–March.

Possum browsing has had a marked effect on the well-being of mistletoes and so they are now not nearly as plentiful as formerly. The species is mainly found on silver beech and black beech but may also parasitise *Metrosideros*, *Pittosporum*, *Myrsine* and several exotic plants such as *Pyrus* and *Rosa*.

Pirinoa

- Hemiparasite on trees.
- Leaves narrowly oval, blunt.

Height:
75–90 cm

Scientific Name:
Tupeia antarctica

Other Names:
(Maori) tupia, kohuorangi

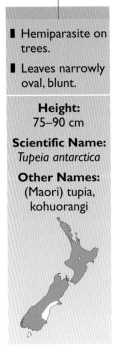

The generic name of this species of mistletoe is believed to be derived from its Maori name of tupia and is the Latinised form of that name, although it could also be from the name of the Tahitian priest, Tupaia, who accompanied Captain Cook from Tahiti to New Zealand in 1769, on his first voyage. Pirinoa is a hemiparasite and is a smaller species of mistletoe than *Peraxilla colensoi* (p. 110), but it will still make a shrub up to a metre or so high. Among the native mistletoe species it is unique because it has only one point of attachment to its host plant, unlike *Peraxilla* or *Ileostylus* (p. 108), which may have several points of attachment to their host plants.

Its rounded branchlets have pale bark and they are clad with narrow leaves that are alternate to more or less opposite, thin and flat, and about 3–5 cm long by 1–3 cm wide; usually they are a rather deepish green and not sharply pointed at their tips. The male and female flowers may be produced on the one plant, or they may be on separate plants. The inflorescences arise from the leaf axils near the ends of the branchlets. The flowers are yellow to yellow-green and the male flowers are a little larger than those of the female. Flowering occurs in October–December. The berries ripen during winter (or they may ripen December–May). They are 5–7 mm wide and are white to pinkish, usually speckled with darker pink or purplish-pink, and they are quite juicy and sticky, which probably assists with their dispersal.

Pirinoa occurs in both the North and South Islands and usually can be found on a variety of hosts including *Pseudopanax*, *Coprosma*, *Carpodetus* and the introduced tree lucerne (*Chamaecytisus palmensis*); it also occurs as a double parasite on other species of mistletoe, such as *Ileostylus micranthus* and *Peraxilla tetrapetalla*. It sometimes quite heavily attacks the tree lucerne, which appears to be a favourite host plant. It can also be seen growing in coastal zones, not far above the high-tide mark, to further inland. As well as being known as pirinoa, it is also referred to as tupia, taapia, kohuorangi, pirita and green mistletoe.

Kumarahou

- Bushy shrub.
- Profuse yellow flowers in flattish clusters.

Height: 2–3 m

Scientific Name:
Pomaderris kumeraho

Other Names:
Gumdigger's soap, Poverty Bay weed

Kumarahou is an interesting shrub that occurs only from North Cape to the Bay of Plenty on the east, and Kawhia harbour on the west.

It usually grows 2–3 m tall but does not have a particularly dense habit. If examined with a hand lens, most parts of the plant, including the backs of its leaves, are seen to be covered with fine, buff hairs, each split at the top into numerous divisions radiating from the centre in a star shape. The leaves are 5–6 by 2–3 cm and are more or less elliptic; their upper surfaces are bluish- to greyish-green and without hairs. The veins form a network and are imprinted into the upper surface.

The bright yellow flowers are produced from the tips of branchlets or from the leaf axils in flattish clusters up to about 10 cm across. The individual flowers are small and about 5 mm wide. Flowering is usually during September–October and the shrubs are smothered with flowers, so much so that the bushes soon exhaust themselves and become debilitated. The flowers are followed by small brownish seed capsules that hold dark brown, shiny seeds.

Kumarahou used to be common in the poor clay soils of kauri gum lands and similar areas, but is now far less common because of the more intensive development of farmland that has occurred over its habitat areas. It is now more restricted to roadside areas. Its specific name is derived from its Maori name, except that in the process of Latinising its name an 'e' was substituted for an 'a' and the final 'u' was dropped, thus making 'kumeraho'. The name of kumarahou was originally more confined to the north of Northland. Its scientific generic name is derived from the Greek *poma*, lid, and *derris*, skin, in reference to the membranous covering of its seed vessel.

The early settlers and gumdiggers gave this shrub the name of gumdiggers' soap, as by taking a handful of flowers and lathering them with water they made a good substitute for soap. That is because the flowers contain saponin, a soapy substance that froths in water. At one stage it was also known as Poverty Bay weed because of its prevalence in that area, and it has also been known as golden tainui.

Pomaderris prunifolia var. *edgerleyi*

- Low-growing shrub.
- Flowers creamy to pale yellow.

Height:
Mainly prostrate

Scientific Name:
Pomaderris prunifolia var. *edgerleyi*

Other Names:
Pomaderris edgerleyi

This is one of the smallest species of *Pomaderris* and it is mostly a prostrate shrub, rarely up to a metre tall. In common with the other species of *Pomaderris*, its branchlets are covered with brownish hairs. When viewed through a hand lens, the top of each hair is seen to be split into numerous divisions radiating from the centre in a star shape. Its leaves all tend to lie in the one plane and they are about 1.5–2.5 cm long by 7–10 mm wide. They are broadly elliptical to slightly oblong; their upper surfaces are a deepish green and the veins are impressed so that their surfaces appear slightly roughened. Their undersurfaces are rather densely covered with whitish hairs, except that the veins are covered with brown hairs, while the margins are slightly toothed at the ends of the veins. The inflorescences are rounded clusters produced from the tips or laterally from just below the tips of its branchlets. The flowers are somewhat creamy-yellow or a pale yellow and are about 3 mm in diameter. Flowering usually takes place in September–October.

Pomaderris prunifolia var. *edgerleyi* occurs from North Cape to North Kaipara Head where it grows in low scrub on poor clay hills. As with a number of other species from Northland, changes to the agricultural scene mean that it is now more likely to be seen on the roadside than anywhere else.

This species does not ever appear to have had a common name, but it has been suggested that it could be referred to as the 'prostrate kumarahou'. It has been known as kumarahou, but the adoption of such a name would create confusion with P. *kumeraho* (p. 114). Its specific name refers to the fancied resemblance of its leaves to some member of the genus *Prunus*, while its varietal name commemorates Englishman John Edgerley, a 19th-century plant collector and nurseryman who migrated to New Zealand.

Poataniwha

Poataniwha is more often seen as a shrub, in rather open situations, although it will attain tree-like dimensions and is capable of growing to about 5 m or so in height. It is one of a group of three unrelated shrubs that all appear to be rather similar but in fact belong to quite different plant families. The other two are the twiggywood (*Raukaua anomalus*, p. 120) and the manuakura (*Melicytus micranthus*).

Poataniwha is generally a low shrub 1–2 m tall with slender, twiggy, dark brown branchlets that tend to be interlacing. On younger plants its leaves are trifoliolate, with one larger terminal leaflet and the two side leaflets smaller. On older plants it has only a single, more or less rounded leaf, the margins of which, along with those of the juveniles, have shallow, rounded teeth. The one character that enables this species to be readily identified is its distinctive leaf stalks. They are flattened and, where they join the leaf blade, a definite joint is visible.

The flowers of poataniwha are grouped in small clusters of one to four and are another distinguishing character because they are about 4–5 mm in diameter and have pale greenish-white to clear white petals. Neither the *Raukaua* nor the *Melicytus* have such readily distinguishable flowers. Flowering usually occurs in September–November. Its small fruits are distinguished by usually having four segments that are initially green before turning brown as they ripen. Inside these seed cases there are shiny black seeds. The fruits are usually ripe during December–April.

Poataniwha is a very distant relation of the orange, both being in the family Rutaceae, and if its leaves are crushed between the fingers minute oil glands cause them to release a very pleasant scent.

This species occurs in lowland forest and around forest margins, in both the North and South Islands, from near North Cape southwards. *Melicope* means 'honey incision', from the Greek *meli*, honey, and *kope*, cutting, in reference to the notched glands of its nectaries. The specific name of *simplex* is from the Latin and refers to the adult plant having only the one simple leaf.

Twiggywood

While this species is similar to poataniwha (p. 118), it is still sufficiently different that it can be readily identified. *Raukaua anomalus* is usually a small, many-branched shrub up to 3 m tall but often much less. It has a divaricating habit and its branches tend to spread at right angles with the branchlets being more or less zigzagging. When growing in forest its branching is more open. It differs from similar species in that its young branchlets are covered with small bristle-like hairs, whereas *Melicope simplex* (p. 118) has smooth branchlets that do not have those obvious bristle-like hairs.

As with *Melicope simplex*, juvenile plants of this species often have trifoliolate leaves with just three small leaflets. Adult plants nearly always have simple leaves that are about 8–20 mm by 5–15 mm. Their upper surfaces are deep green and have a dark blotch at their bases where the stalk joins the blade. The margins are bluntly toothed or lobed, and they may also be slightly notched at the tips. The greenish flowers of twiggywood are very small and are produced in small clusters of up to four flowers. The fruits are about 4–5 mm in diameter, rounded and much flattened, bearing the remains of part of the flower at the top. They are usually white, speckled with dark bluish-purple, but may also be speckled with brown or even the whole fruit will ripen to brown.

Twiggywood occurs in the North, South and Stewart Islands where it is found in lowland to montane forests and scrub from about Kaitaia southwards. Its generic name is the Latinised form of raukawa, the Maori name for R. *edgerleyi*, another member of this genus. The specific name of *anomalus* is from the Greek *anomalos*, meaning abnormal or irregular, because it is so different from the two other members of the genus.

Corokia cotoneaster

- Twiggy shrub, branchlets interlaced.
- Fruits dark red or red to orange/yellow.

Height: 2–2.5 m

Scientific Name:
Corokia cotoneaster

Corokia cotoneaster is another of our unique divaricating plants, forming a stiff shrub up to about 2–2.5 m tall, with interlacing branches that can be quite tangled. Its bark is rather dark, being almost black, and its branchlets tend to zigzag. The young branchlets are thickly covered with whitish hairs, as are the backs of its leaves. According to where it grows, the leaves may vary in size but, generally, they are more or less spoon-shaped, from 2–15 mm long by 2–10 mm at their widest part, and they are on flattened stalks up to 2 cm long. Their upper surfaces are a deep, shiny green or sometimes a bronzy colour.

The small starry flowers are 5–8 mm in diameter and have pointed petals. They are bright yellow and are produced either singly or in few-flowered clusters from near the tips of the branchlets. Generally, *Corokia cotoneaster* flowers during September–November, but it may have occasional flowers on it for much of the year. They are followed by berry-like fruits about 5–8 mm long. Their colours vary from dark red to red to orange or yellow. Sometimes a selection of the various coloured fruits may be found in the one area. Like the flowers, the fruits may be found on the bushes for most of the year, especially February–May. They last on the bush for quite a long time, often until late in the winter.

Corokia cotoneaster occurs throughout most of New Zealand from the Three Kings Islands southwards. In the South Island it is more common east of the Southern Alps. It occurs in a variety of habitats in lowland scrublands, rocky areas, hill country and forest margins as well as light open forest. The species ascends from sea level to about 900 m.

Its specific name is due to its resemblance to some species of the garden shrub *Cotoneaster*, which receives its name from the Latin *cotone*, a quince, and *aster*, a wild or an inferior kind, because of its similarity to quince. The generic name is formed from the Maori name korokio. In New Zealand, in spite of being so common, it has never had a recognised common name, although wiry corokia, a colloquialism that was recorded in 1915, is possibly more appropriate. In the United Kingdom it is generally known as the New Zealand wire-netting bush.

New Zealand celery

New Zealand celery is common around the coast throughout most of the country and is actually a relation of the common garden celery (*Apium graveolens*). It is a perennial herb with a stout and deeply descending taproot that can be up to 3 cm in diameter. It may be seen either as a plant with a single crown or it can be branched with a number of crowns to form quite large plants.

The leaves are much divided, after the fashion of the garden celery, and they are also of a similar deep green. Each leaf is on a stout stalk up to 10 cm long with a sheathing base that wraps around the rootstock. The leaf blade is usually divided two or three times, while the individual segments are deeply cut or lobed and their margins are toothed. Small, white flowers are produced in clusters up to 15 mm in diameter and may be seen on the plant in December–February. While not as strongly scented as garden celery, New Zealand celery still has a distinctive celery smell.

Apium prostratum is found on coastal rocks and banks as well as in sandy areas, often growing within the splash zone. The species occurs from the Kermadec and Three Kings Islands around the coastlines of the North, South and Stewart Islands, the Chatham Islands and south to the Antipodes Islands. It is also quite widely spread around the southern hemisphere.

Apparently, Maori did not regard New Zealand celery as a culinary vegetable and used it only for medicinal purposes. They may also have used it for vapour baths. It was not until Captain James Cook arrived in this country in 1769 that it became appreciated for its anti-scorbutic (scurvy-preventing) properties. Cook had large quantities of it gathered so as to feed it to his crew for its preventative and curative properties. Following Cook's example, other seafarers made liberal use of New Zealand celery as an anti-scorbutic. Its Maori name is tutaekoau and it also has several Pakeha common names: celery, native celery, prostrate celery (from its lowly habit of growth), sea celery (from its habitat) and Maori celery being the usual ones.

Sea holly

Although the genus *Eryngium*, or sea holly, has over 200 species around the world, we have only the one species, as happens with a number of native plants. *Eryngium vesiculosum* is an interesting plant that is confined to coastal areas around the North Island and the northern half of the South Island. It is also a native of Australia and has occasionally been referred to as the Australian sea holly, small sea holly, eryngo, which is an alternative northern hemisphere name for *Eryngium*, or vesiculate eryngium, this last really being an Anglicised version of its scientific name. Nobody has been able to provide a more appropriate vernacular name and, for want of anything better, it appears that 'sea holly' is probably the most appropriate common name for it.

It is a prickly little herb that has a deep taproot which sends out numerous stolons or rhizomes to form reasonably large patches up to 60 cm or more across. The taproot is surrounded by a rosette of numerous leaves, and where each stolon roots into the ground a new rosette is formed. The leaves are long and narrow, more or less 5–15 cm long, and somewhat spoon-shaped towards their tips. They are pale green to glaucous and sometimes slightly bronze coloured. Their margins are somewhat undulating and are deeply toothed or lobed with pungent prickles. The stalks that bear the flower heads may be up to 5 cm long, but often the flower heads tend to sit down among the leaves. They are more or less globular and up to 2 cm in diameter. Each flower head has up to 15–20 minute flowers and is surrounded with narrow spiny bracts (modified leaves) that project out from beneath the head.

Sea holly occurs in both the North and South Islands where it grows in coastal sands and gravels as well as occasionally in rock clefts. It is also found at one or two inland lowland localities such as the drainage areas of the Hurunui River and the Waimakariri River, in Canterbury.

Koheriki

- Much-branched perennial herb or subshrub.

- Small, white flowers in largish heads.

Height:
50 cm to 1 m

Scientific Name:
Scandia rosifolia

Koheriki is a perennial herb, but because the lower parts of its stems are often rather woody, it may alternatively be regarded as a subshrub. In a more open situation it may grow as a smaller bushy plant up to about 50 cm tall, but in other situations it grows as a scrambling plant, usually up to a metre tall; it uses other plants for support, or may scramble over rocks, depending on the situation.

The young growing portion of the stem is quite glaucous. Koheriki is much-branched with leaves scattered along its stems at fairly regular intervals. The leaf stalks have a distinct sheathing base that is often a pinkish-purple colour and clasps the stem. The leaves are 5–12.5 cm long and have two to five pairs of leaflets, while the leaflets have no stalks. Its petioles (main leaf stalks) are grooved. The leaflets are 2.5–6.5 cm long by about 2.5–3 cm wide with the terminal leaflet being distinctly larger; their upper surfaces are bright green and shiny, they have finely and sharply toothed margins and their tips are acute. Particularly on their upper surfaces, there is a beautifully marked system of finely reticulated veins.

When koheriki flowers, it produces, from near the tips of its branches, quite large heads of small, white flowers up to about 8 cm in diameter. They are on stalks about 3 cm long. It usually flowers during September–November. The schizocarps (dry fruits or seeds) are about 3 mm long and are typical of members of the Apiaceae.

Koheriki is found on the Three Kings Islands and in the North Island southwards to about North Taranaki on the western side, and to about Napier on the eastern side. It mainly occurs in lowland coastal and rocky places, and along stream-sides; it appears to be absent from the Bay of Plenty coast. The species ranges from sea level to about 620 m.

The introduced possum is apparently quite fond of it and accounts for its scarcity in some regions.

Bush snowberry/Takapo

Gaultheria antipoda is probably the most common species of snowberry and it may be seen in a range of situations around New Zealand. It can vary from a low shrub, often only about 60–70 cm tall, to one that may be up to 2 m tall, and it has differently coloured fruits. The genus *Gaultheria* is named in honour of an 18th-century physician and botanist of Québec, Dr Jean-François Gaultier (also spelt Gaulthier).

Bush snowberry is often a rather sparse shrub whose reddish-brown branchlets are covered with a mixture of black, bristly hairs intermixed with pale, shorter downy hairs. The leaves are alternate, 5–12 mm by 5–10 mm, more or less rounded, their upper surfaces deep green and shiny, rather stiff and thickened with toothed margins and their undersurfaces paler. On both their surfaces there is an obvious network of veins.

The white, bell-shaped flowers are produced singly from the leaf axils towards the tips of its branchlets. Flowering usually occurs during November–December, with some plants occasionally having flowers as late as February. After flowering its berry-like fruits develop. What appears to be a succulent berry is the flower's calyx becoming swollen and fleshy so that it encloses the thin, dry seed capsule, containing many seeds. The colour of these fruits may be deep crimson, red, pink or pure white. Plants fruit mainly during January–April, but fruits may appear on some plants over much of the year.

Bush snowberry is found throughout most of the North, South and Stewart Islands where it occurs in lowland to montane forest and scrub and shrublands. It often grows on rock faces and in rocky places.

The specific name *antipoda* refers to it growing throughout New Zealand, which is regarded as the antipodes of Great Britain. *Gaultheria antipoda* has a number of common names, including chuckie chucks, a name dating back to 1856 but of unknown derivation; false beech snowberry, because of the resemblance of its leaves to those of silver beech (*Nothofagus menziesii*); nardoo berry, a name dating to the 1860s, possibly of Australian derivation but of unknown origin; and the Maori names takapo, koropeka and tawiniwini, the last said to be a Stewart Island name.

Mingimingi (*Leptecophylla juniperina*)

- Erect, bushy shrub.
- Narrow, needle-sharp leaves.

Height: 1–1.5 m

Scientific Name: *Leptecophylla juniperina*

Other Names: Prickly mingimingi, mikimiki

Leptecophylla juniperina is one of several shrubs that Maori referred to as mingimingi without distinguishing one species from the other. It may be recognised by its very narrow, needle-sharp leaves as well as its greyish, almost black stems. It is usually an erect and densely branched shrub growing to 1–1.5 m tall. In some rather exposed situations, such as on rock bluffs, it may be only about 60 cm tall.

The leaves are mostly spreading to slightly reflexed, very narrow and 7–20 mm long by 1–2 mm wide, green to yellowish-green or sometimes with bronzy-green upper surfaces, while their undersurfaces are slightly glaucous. They taper to a pungent point, which can be quite sharp.

The small, bell-shaped white flowers are only about 3 mm long, and are produced singly from the leaf axils or from the tips of the branchlets. Mingimingi may flower in August–December, but the main flowering period is during October–November. The berry-like fruit may be 5–9 mm wide. The fruits have a slightly flattened appearance at the top and bottom and their thin flesh is inclined to have a rather dry texture, while each fruit contains five hard seeds.

The colour of the fruits varies from a deep crimson to red, pink or white. While fruits on a bush may be of a uniform colour, those of adjacent bushes may be quite different. Plants of this species growing in the far north or in western districts of both islands, especially in Otago and Southland, are more robust and have larger fruits than those that grow in eastern districts. The fruits are particularly noticeable during February–May.

Mingimingi occurs in the North, South and Stewart Islands where it grows in lowland to montane forests. It can be quite common in forests, scrub and shrub-lands. In some parts common sites for it are on rock faces and bluffs or in stony areas. This species also occurs in Tasmania and in south-eastern Australia.

It has been favoured with some 16 common names. Prickly mingimingi is one author's invention while mingimingi is a North Island variant, with mikimiki being its South Island dialectal form. Both names have been shortened to mingi or miki or even mikimik. Other Maori names are inangaporiro or inakaporiro (South Island dialect), tumingi or taumingi. Its specific name is derived from the similarity of its leaves to those of some species of *Juniperus*.

Mingimingi (*Leucopogon fasciculatus*)

- **Openly branched shrub.**
- **Dull green leaves; tips not sharp.**

Height: 1–5 m

Scientific Name:
Leucopogon fasciculatus

Other Names:
(Maori) tumingi

In contrast to *Leptecophylla juniperina* (p. 132), this mingimingi, *Leucopogon fasciculatus*, is a more openly branched shrub that may grow to about 5 m tall, although often it is shorter than this. Its leaves are softer and hardly prickly, because they do not have pungent tips. Also, its flowers are borne in pendant spikes rather than singly as with *Leptecophylla juniperina*. Formerly, the species was classified in the genus *Cyathodes*.

Leucopogon fasciculatus tends to be a spreading shrub with wiry branches and branchlets, rather than being stiff and erect. The bark is dark brown and inclined to be rough. Its leaves are usually a dull green on their upper surfaces, the undersurfaces paler, measuring 10–15 mm long by 2–4 mm wide (though on juvenile plants they may be considerably larger), and their tips are barely pungent, if at all. The flowers are greenish-white, more or less bell-shaped, about 3 mm in diameter and are produced on pendant racemes about 1–3 cm long, each bearing six to twelve flowers. Flowering may occur during August–December and the fruits are produced September–March. They are rather small, red, only about 2–3 mm in diameter and, on the bush, they are not as spectacular as those of *Leptecophylla juniperina*.

Leucopogon fasciculatus is quite widely distributed, occurring on the Three Kings Islands, throughout the North Island and in the South Island to about as far south as Banks Peninsula on the east coast and to about Hokitika on the west coast. It can be rather local in its distribution. It is often associated with beech forest where it can be quite common.

This is another plant that the Maori referred to as mingimingi or mikimiki. It is also called tumingi. Its generic name of *Leucopogon* means white beard, from the Greek *leukos*, white, and *pogon*, a beard, referring to the insides of the lobes around the mouth of its flowers being densely bearded. The specific name of *fasciculatus* is from the Latin *fasciculus*, meaning fascicled or arranged in small bundles, and refers to its flowers being in small clusters.

Hangehange

- **Much-branched, bushy shrub.**
- **Bright green leaves.**

Height: 3 m

Scientific Name:
Geniostoma ligustrifolium

Other Names:
New Zealand privet;
(Maori) papahenga

Hangehange, a forest shrub of rather undistinguished appearance, has been treated as one species, but there has been recent discussion as to whether at least two other entities or varieties should possibly be recognised.

As generally regarded, hangehange is a much-branched, bushy shrub up to about 3 m tall with a more or less erect habit of growth. All parts of it are smooth and green and without hairs of any kind. Its slender, rounded branches are rather brittle and easily broken.

The leaves are 4–7.5 cm long by 2–3.2 cm wide, their upper surfaces are usually a bright green and they are paler beneath. Their margins are entire and the tips of the leaves are drawn out to a point. The leaf stalks are about 4–10 mm long. On young growths the leaves are a pale green but become darker with age. The pale greenish flowers are 4–6 mm wide and are produced in small clusters from the leaf axils. Their short corolla lobes or petals are spreading or reflexed. Although they are not overly conspicuous on the shrub, they have a delicious and heavy scent that can be detected at some distance from the plant. Flowering usually occurs September–November. The seed capsules are produced after flowering; they are about 7 mm long and split into two lobes when ripe.

Hangehange is an abundant shrub in coastal to lowland forest areas, particularly where there has been some clearance or disturbance. It occurs on the Three Kings Islands (now considered to be a separate variety) and throughout most of the coastal and lowland areas of the North Island. A distinctive form that grows on the Surville Cliffs at North Cape is also considered to be a separate variety. Like a few other northern species, hangehange just makes an appearance in the South Island and is found around parts of the Marlborough Sounds, in northern Nelson at Pepin Island, near Totaranui and at one or two other coastal sites in north-western Nelson.

The generic name *Geniostoma* is derived from the Greek *geneion*, beard, and *stoma*, mouth, which alludes to the hairy throat of the flower. Its specific name of *ligustrifolium* alludes to its resemblance to the common privet or *Ligustrum*.

136

New Zealand jasmine / Kaiwhiria

Parsonsia capsularis is a stem-twining climbing plant that may be recognised by its opposite leaves having a pronounced bump where their leaf stalks join onto the stem. It is quite a variable species with a number of different forms occurring in various parts of the country. This species appears to be more frequent in scrublands and around forest outskirts than its relation, P. *heterophylla* (p. 140), which is more likely to be found as a forest climber.

It is a twining plant that climbs over small trees and shrubs. Its slender branches are dark coloured and, while its leaves may be variable, on any particular plant they are generally uniform. On adult plants they are fairly narrow, or narrowly spear-shaped to more oblong, 2–10 cm long by 2.5–10 mm wide, their margins are usually even or sinuate with small lobes and, when young, they are often brownish and mottled; their tips may be blunt or pointed.

The flowers are on branched clusters produced from the leaf axils or from the tips of the branchlets. According to district, and the particular form being observed, the flowers may vary from white through to yellow, or pink through to a deep red, rose or pink. The flowers are fragrant and about 5 mm in diameter, the corolla lobes (petals) usually being slightly curled backwards. Flowering normally occurs during September–February.

After flowering, the seed pods, 6–10 cm long, are particularly noticeable. When ripe these capsules split open from their tips and release their blackish seeds, each of which has a parachute of silvery hairs that enables it to waft away on the breeze. Apparently, the seeds will always land on the ground in an upright position, because the parachute hairs have a lower ring of downward-facing hairs that enables them to do just that. The seed pods (inset photo) usually ripen in November–April, although the old, empty pods remain visible on plants even well into the winter.

This New Zealand jasmine occurs in the North and South Islands, where it is found around coastal to montane forest margins and in scrublands. *Parsonsia* is named to commemorate Dr John Parsons (1705–1770), a Scottish physician and writer on natural history. The specific name of *capsularis* means having capsules and is derived from the Latin *capsula*, a box.

New Zealand jasmine/ Kaihua

Like *Parsonia capsularis* (p. 138), this is a rather variable plant. It is probably the most common of the species of New Zealand jasmine. P. *heterophylla* is a relatively tall climbing plant that will ascend to about 10 m, but in more open situations it may sprawl over surrounding shrubs.

On young seedling plants the usually reddish-brown leaves may be long and narrow with more or less even margins, or the margins may be sinuate or with rounded lobes; once a plant attains maturity they are about 4–8 cm long by 1–4 cm wide. They become shorter and broader but may still be somewhat variable in shape. Generally, they are spear-shaped, pointed at their tips, and their texture is leathery, while their upper surfaces are deep green and somewhat shiny.

The scented flowers are mainly white, but yellow forms may be seen in some districts. The flowers are up to 7 mm long, produced in many-flowered inflorescences that arise from the leaf axils or the tips of the branchlets. One author has likened their scent to that of cucumber, but it is definitely a much sweeter perfume than that. Flowering may occur in September–March, although it does so mainly during spring and early summer. The seed pods are 7–15 cm long and usually form in December–April. When ripe, as with P. *capsularis*, each pod splits open from its tip so as to release its blackish seeds with their fluffy parachutes.

P. *heterophylla* occurs on the Three Kings Islands and throughout the North, South and Stewart Islands, growing in coastal to lowland and lower montane forests. Often it is more a plant of forest margins and it may also be seen in some scrubby areas or even growing on rock faces. The species ranges from sea level to 900 m.

While New Zealand jasmine is probably its most used common name, to Maori it is known as kaihua or kaiwhiria, as well as having other names, and when it was fashionable to add the prefix 'Maori' to so many plants it was also known as Maori jasmine. Its specific name of *heterophylla* means with differing leaves and is from the Greek *heteros*, various or diverse, and *phullon*, leaf, referring to the diverse leaf shapes on juvenile plants.

- Erect to spreading shrub.
- Orange fruits, largest of coprosmas.

Height: To 3 m

Scientific Name:
Coprosma foetidissima

Although capable of growing into a small tree, hupiro is more often seen as a shrub up to about 3 m tall. Its growth is fairly erect to somewhat spreading, and generally it is more openly branched and does not form a particularly dense shrub except in open situations. The bark is a rather dark brown, but on the young branchlets it is paler.

The leaves are more or less oblong, about 2–5 cm long by 1–2 cm wide, their upper surfaces are medium to dark green, somewhat shiny, and they have blunt tips and are on winged stalks. On the lower surfaces, along each side of the midrib, there are several small pits (known as domatia); these domatia are visible on the upper surface as small raised bumps. If you brush against hupiro, the leaves emit the plant's distinctive bad smell.

The female flowers are solitary at the tips of short branchlets and flowering is usually during mid- to late spring. Its fruits are among the largest of the coprosmas and are 7–10 mm long, but because they are only produced singly they do not make a spectacular display such as is seen on many other species of *Coprosma*. The fruits are usually ripe in March–April.

Hupiro occurs throughout the North, South and Stewart Islands and then to the subantarctic Auckland Islands. It grows in coastal, montane and subalpine forest and scrub from Moehau southwards but, in the North Island, is absent from Mt Taranaki. The species ranges from sea level to 1370 m.

The genus *Coprosma* receives its name from the foetid smell that some species emit; it is derived from the Greek *kopros*, dung, and *osme*, odour or perfume. This plant's specific name of *foetidissima* is from the Latin *foetidus*, meaning stinking, and is very appropriate for this species.

Karangu

■ One of our
tallest shrubs;
shiny, leathery
leaves.

■ Orange to
orange-red
fruits.

Height: 6 m

Scientific Name:
Coprosma lucida

Other names:
(Maori) karamu

Of the more than 45 species of *Coprosma* native to New Zealand, this is one of the more common forest species. It is a shrub of forest undergrowth, but it may also be seen in more open situations, such as some scrubby areas and even on rock faces. This species is similar to, and confused with, the common karamu, C. *robusta* (p. 150). Maori did not distinguish between the two and both were referred to as karamu, kakaramu and karamuramu, while European authors have referred to C. *lucida* confusingly as glossy karamu or shining karamu.

Karangu forms a shrub, or even a small tree, up to about 6 m tall. Its leaves are 7–16 cm long by 3–5 cm wide, on stalks about 3 cm long. They may be narrowly to broadly elliptic, usually widest above their middles, tough and leathery, their upper surfaces deep green and shiny and somewhat pointed at their tips. Between the pairs of leaves, where they join the stem, is a pair of small scale-like appendages with a triangular shape and dark, tooth-like processes at their apexes; they are known as stipules. These stipules, present on all coprosmas, differ according to the species and are useful in their identification. In this instance, the stipule is relatively broad in relation to its length.

Like all *Coprosma* species, the male and female flowers are on separate plants and they are wind pollinated. Male flowers are produced in dense clusters on branched or unbranched stalks and their anthers dangle down on quite long filaments so that the pollen is easily distributed by the wind. The female flowers are in clusters of three or four on three-forked stalks. Flowering usually occurs during the spring months. After pollination its berry-like, orange to orange-red fruits begin to form and they are about 8–11 mm long when ripe.

Karangu is found throughout the North, South and Stewart Islands where it occurs in coastal, lowland and montane scrub and forests from near North Cape southwards. It grows from sea level to about 1000 m and often occurs as an epiphyte. Its specific name of *lucida* means bright or shining and comes from the Latin *lucidus*, lux or light. *Coprosma lucida* was discovered in Queen Charlotte Sound during Cook's second voyage to New Zealand (1772–75) and, incidentally, was the first species of *Coprosma* to be discovered.

- Densely bushy, twiggy shrub.
- Small, narrow, dark green leaves.

Height: 1–5 m

Scientific Name: *Coprosma propinqua*

This species is another of those twiggy, divaricating shrubs that Maori lumped together under the common name of mingimingi or mikimiki. The common European name of black scrub appears to have arisen from the generally blackish or dark green appearance exhibited by this species, particularly when viewed from a distance.

Coprosma propinqua is a rather variable, bushy shrub, usually growing from about 1 m to sometimes up to 5 m tall. In exposed sites in coastal habitats it may sometimes be dwarfed to an almost prostrate or mat-like shrub.

The bark of older branches is generally grey. The small, dark-green and glossy leaves usually have a fairly thick texture; they are usually 10–14 mm long by about 3 mm or so wide. The bases of the leaf stipules are joined so that they form a short sheath around the stem, and usually they have a single small tooth at the tip of each stipule. The male flowers are usually produced singly from the tips of short branchlets and the female flowers grow in clusters of one to four from the leaf axils of very short branchlets. Its fruits are 5–7 mm long and are translucent, varying from pale to dark blue, often flecked with a darker blue. In this respect the species of *Coprosma* are unusual in that they display such a wide range of fruit colours.

Black scrub occurs in coastal and lowland to montane shrublands, scrub, forest and swamplands or stony and rocky areas throughout the North, South and Stewart Islands from Mangonui southwards, but is absent from Taranaki. There are also two varieties of C. *propinqua*, one of which is confined to the Chatham Islands.

The species was discovered in 1833 by Allan Cunningham in shaded woods at 'wangaroa' (Whangaroa) in Northland. Cunningham spent five months in 1826 in Northland, collecting plants, and his brother Richard retraced Allan's journey in 1833.

Its specific name of *propinqua* means related and implies that it has a close resemblance to another species, C. *parviflora*, which occurs in the North Island. C. *propinqua*, in common with most other *Coprosma* species, hybridises quite freely with larger-leaved species such as C. *robusta* (p. 150), the resulting hybrids being known as C. ×*cunninghamii*.

Coprosma rhamnoides

- Twiggy, bushy shrub.

- Young stems pale, curved downwards.

Height: 1–2 m

Scientific Name: *Coprosma rhamnoides*

Other Names: Twiggy coprosma

This is one of the numerous shrubby species of *Coprosma* that have a twiggy habit and small leaves, quite unlike the large-leaved species such as C. *lucida* (p. 144). Although quite a common species, it has never achieved enough notice to warrant a common name other than twiggy coprosma.

Generally, this is a small, spreading shrub up to 1–2 m tall. Its bark is reddish-brown to grey-brown and it has stiff, interlaced branches and branchlets. In forest it often has a more open habit, whereas in open situations it is usually more compact and the curving tips of its almost leafless young branchlets are rather spine-like; in forest situations, that character is either absent or almost so. On some forms of this species the tips of these young branchlets may be either a pale, almost whitish colour or even quite yellowish.

The leaves are of various shapes from trowel-shaped to broad or almost round, and bushes can frequently exhibit all shapes on the one plant, although occasional bushes may tend to have leaves mostly of uniform shape and size. Its small leaves have bluntish tips, they are 7–12 mm by 4–14 mm and may be green to a brownish-green and frequently have pale blotches on them. Flowers are produced from the leaf axils: the male flowers in clusters of two to four while the female flowers are solitary. Flowering occurs mainly during the spring months (usually about October). Its berry-like drupes are 3–4 mm in diameter, small and round, and may be red, dark red or even almost black. Fruiting mainly occurs in March–April, although fruits may sometimes be seen on bushes throughout much of the year.

Coprosma rhamnoides occurs in the North, South and Stewart Islands where it grows in lowland to lower montane forests and shrublands. In some areas it is quite widespread and, as already stated, can be a baffling species because it exists in quite a variety of forms. For example, in the southern South Island and on Stewart Island, the leaves of some forms can be so narrow that such plants appear to belong almost to another species. Usually, the typically downward curve of its young branchlets is sufficient to indicate that it is C. *rhamnoides*. Its specific name of *rhamnoides* is chosen because it resembles a species of R*hamnus* or buckthorn shrub.

Karamu

Karamu is a fairly sturdy and usually erect shrub or even a small tree that is quite common throughout much of New Zealand. It is one of the larger-leaved species of *Coprosma*, similar to C. *lucida* (p. 144), which some people confuse with karamu, especially when there are no flowers or fruits to aid identification. Its specific name of *robusta* is from the Latin, *robustus*, meaning stout or strong in growth.

The leaves are noticeably thinner compared with those of C. *lucida* and are 7–12 cm long by 3–4 cm wide. They are broadly elliptic or slightly oblong-elliptic and are broadest about their middles, whereas those of C. *lucida* are broadest above their middles. The upper surfaces of the leaves of karamu are deep green and somewhat shiny, but not as markedly so as those of C. *lucida*. One of the key factors in its identification is the shape of the stipules that connect its leaf stalks. Those of karamu are united at their bases and they are longer and narrower than those of C. *lucida*, while their black-tipped, tooth-like processes are quite long and drawn out.

The male flowers are in many-flowered clusters borne on short stalks. The female flowers are in compound clusters that arise from the leaf axils. Flowering occurs during the spring months, usually when the spring winds blow, so that its pollen has the greatest chance of reaching the female flowers. Its berry-like drupes are usually orange or orange-red and they are in quite dense clusters. Each fruit is about 5–9 mm long. Fruiting usually occurs during March–April.

Karamu is distributed from the Three Kings Islands and throughout the North and South Islands, but in the South Island it is apparently not found south of about Oamaru on the eastern side. It grows in lowland and montane forests and in shrublands from sea level to 1200 m and is one of the more widely distributed of the *Coprosma* species, as well as becoming naturalised on the Chatham Islands.

Niniao

Although at present included in the genus *Helichrysum*, this species, along with New Zealand's other species of *Helichrysum*, is, as the result of further botanical studies, likely to be assigned to another genus. *Helichrysum* includes the familiar everlasting flowers but none of the native species bears any resemblance to an everlasting flower. The generic name is derived from the Greek *helios*, the sun, and *chrysos*, golden. The specific name for niniao, *lanceolatum*, means spear-shaped and refers to the shape of the leaves, but in this case its leaves are usually anything but spear-shaped.

Niniao is an erect, densely divaricating shrub of up to 3 m in height with brown bark and quite thin, twiggy branchlets that can be rather whippy. Its smallish leaves are generally roundish, about 2–4 cm long by 1.5–3 cm wide, their upper surfaces are a light to medium green and their undersurfaces are whitish because they are covered with a dense whitish or greyish mat of closely interlaced hairs. Its flowers are in tightly bunched balls or clusters on short branchlets. They are creamy-coloured and there are about eight to twelve little flowers in each cluster. Flowering usually occurs during October–January.

Niniao grows in the North and South Islands from the Northland peninsula to the south of the South Island. It is a shrub of light, more or less open forest and scrub and often grows around forest margins and on rocky banks. It seems to favour growing in dry bush. The species ranges from sea level to about 900 m. Plants from different areas tend to vary somewhat; for example, those from the serpentine area around the Surville Cliffs at North Cape are quite a distinct variety.

Somewhere along the line a form that had more or less lanceolate leaves was discovered, hence the reason for its current name, *lanceolatum*. Originally, its specific name was from the Latin *glomerata*, which was more appropriate because it referred to its ball-like clusters of flowers referred to as a glomerule. At one stage it was also named H. *aggregatum*, because its flowers were aggregated into ball-like heads, but that name has also been superseded.

Anaphalis trinervis

This is one of those native species of everlasting daisy that are very showy when in flower. It was transferred to *Anaphalis* because it did not sit comfortably with its former genus, *Gnaphalium*, or the cudweeds as they are commonly known.

Anaphalis trinervis is a somewhat stout plant. The bases of its stems are woody, but towards their tips they are rather soft. Generally, it is a creeping or trailing plant, but its growing tips are more or less erect or ascending, and it may grow to about 25 cm or so tall. Its leaves are 5–10 cm long by 1–2 cm wide, and they are more or less lanceolate and usually widest above their middles. Their upper surfaces are deep green and shiny, while the lower surfaces are clad with a tightly appressed covering of silvery-white hairs.

The flower heads are produced in clusters and the individual heads are about 1.5 cm in diameter. The bracts surrounding each flower head are white and papery. The individual florets comprising each head are yellow. Flowering usually occurs during November–January.

Anaphalis trinervis occurs in the North and South Islands where it is generally found growing in damp and shaded places, such as moist and shady banks. In the North Island it occurs from about the central ranges southwards. It is more common in the South Island, especially west of the Southern Alps.

Anaphalis derives its name from the classical Greek name for another of the everlasting flowers, while its specific name of *trinervis* refers to the three prominent veins on its leaves. This species was first discovered in Dusky Sound by either Johann Reinhold Forster or his son Johann Georg Forster, both of whom accompanied Captain Cook as botanists on his second voyage to New Zealand during 1772–75.

Maakoako

- Creeping and spreading herb.
- White flowers from leaf axils.

Height:
8–10 cm

Scientific Name:
Samolus repens

Other Names:
Sea primrose

Maakoako is an easily recognised, dainty little plant that occurs in coastal areas around most of New Zealand. It is low-growing up to about 8–10 cm high with stems that may sprawl along the ground for up to 30–40 cm. It may grow as an isolated plant or be part of broad matted patches. Its stems are much-branched and often root into the ground as they sprawl over it.

The fleshy leaves are variable in size, measuring 5–15 mm long by 2–8 mm wide. They are usually alternate, but may be clustered. They are broadest towards their tips and their upper surfaces are a light to medium green, while the undersurfaces are paler. Maakoako has solitary, small white flowers about 6–12 mm wide that arise from its leaf axils. The flowering period is quite long, usually from November to about February. Its seed capsules are about 4–5 mm long, but they are not particularly noticeable.

Maakoako occurs on the Kermadec Islands and in coastal regions throughout the North, South, Stewart, Chatham and Auckland Islands. It is common in salt marshes and on rocks. In the South Island it also occurs in one or two inland locations such as the Waipara River in North Canterbury. In addition to New Zealand it also occurs in Australia (including Tasmania), New Caledonia and on Easter Island.

The generic name of *Samolus* is a Latin name said to be of Celtic origin, while the specific name of *repens* means creeping and refers to its lowly habit of growth. Interestingly, this is the only member of the primrose family (Primulaceae) that is represented in the New Zealand flora. Various authors have also named it Maori water-pimpernel and marsh pimpernel, both inappropriate common names for a plant that is not a pimpernel and does not have even a passing resemblance to the northern hemisphere pimpernel.

Remuremu / Rekoreko

- **Widely creeping herb.**

- **Flowers white, split open along one side.**

Height:
2–4 cm

Scientific Name:
Selliera radicans

Other Names:
(Maori) raumangu

Selliera is a southern hemisphere genus (also found in Australia, Tasmania and Chile) that has only one species in New Zealand. S. *radicans*, remuremu, is an easily recognised creeping plant that often forms extensive flat mats in salt marsh areas. Its stems root into the ground, at the nodes, and are usually much interlaced.

The flattish, slightly succulent leaves are solitary or in clusters of up to four. Depending upon site conditions, they may be either erect or pressed against the ground and are club-shaped, 7–30 mm long by 3–8 mm wide, bright green and shiny with blunt tips. The solitary white flowers are abundantly produced over a period of two or three months or even longer. They have yellow in their throats and are curiously one-sided as though split open along one side. Flowering may occur during November–April. The fruit that follows is a fleshy capsule about 6–10 mm long. When ripe it changes to brown.

Remuremu occurs mainly around coastal areas of the North, South and Stewart Islands where it is common in salt meadows and marshlands as well as rocky places near the sea. In the North Island it also occurs around the central Volcanic Plateau, where it grows in wet ground along streams, around tarns and lake margins in the Ruapehu and Tongariro area, as well as on the slopes of the Kaimanawa Mountains. In the South Island it may also be found around lake, stream and tarn margins from southern Nelson and Marlborough southwards to North and Central Otago. The species ranges from sea level to 1000 m.

The *Selliera* genus was named in honour of François Noël Sellier (1737–*c*.1800) who engraved botanical illustrations for the firm of Cavanilles and Desfontaines between 1780 and 1800. Its specific name of *radicans* is from the Latin *radix*, a root, meaning creeping and rooting in reference to its habit.

Waiuatua

- Twiggy, openly branched shrub.

- Flowers bright orange-red to orange.

Height:
60 cm to 1.8 m

Scientific Name:
Rhabdothamnus solandri

Other Names:
(Maori) kaikaiatua, matata, taurepo

The genus *Rhabdothamnus* contains just one species and is confined to New Zealand. It is also our only member of the Gesneriaceae, a largely subtropical and tropical plant family that finds its southernmost limit in New Zealand.

Waiuatua is a slender, twiggy shrub from 60 cm up to 1.8 m or more tall and all parts of it are covered with fine greyish hairs. It is much-branched, although not densely so, and usually rather open. Its rounded leaves are opposite, 1.5–4 cm by 1.5–3 cm, medium green with a darkish appearance caused by a darkening of the veins, while their margins are coarsely toothed.

The flowers are produced singly from the leaf axils, on slender stalks 2–4 cm long. Their colour varies from bright orange-red to orange or sometimes a yellowish colour with reddish stripes. The anthers, bearing the pollen, protrude from the upper portion of each newly opened flower, but are not in a position to pollinate the stigma because they are immature. When the anthers are mature they are positioned so that when a bird pushes its head into the flower tube to take nectar it cannot avoid receiving pollen on its forehead, thus when the next flower is visited the stigma of that flower can be pollinated. The main pollinators are tui, bellbirds, stitchbirds and silvereyes. Especially in northern areas, plants with some flowers on them may be found throughout most of the year.

Waiuatua is found in coastal and lowland forests throughout the North Island from North Cape to the Wellington area but is rather rare and local to the south of Wanganui. Plants growing on the islands offshore from Northland generally have larger leaves than those of the mainland. It was first discovered, in Mercury Bay, by Joseph Banks and Daniel Carlsson Solander in 1769.

Rhabdothamnus derives its name from the Greek *rhabdos*, a rod or wand, and *thamnos*, bush, referring to its rod-like branches. The specific name *solandri* honours Solander, who sailed with James Cook on his first voyage to New Zealand in 1768–71. The species is also known as kaikaiatua, matata and taurepo. Other, rather unlikely names include forest abutilon, for it is not an *Abutilon*, and greenhouse gloxinia, for although the species belongs to the same family as the greenhouse gloxinia, it bears no resemblance to that plant.

- Creeping maritime herb.

- Bright green, kidney-shaped leaves.

Height:
3–5 cm

Scientific Name:
Calystegia soldanella

Other Names:
Sand convolvulus, shore convolvulus, shore bindweed

Calystegia soldanella or panahi is a sand-dwelling species that is familiar around the shores of much of New Zealand. Its creeping and branching stems are usually buried in the sand so that all that can be seen are its leaves and flowers. The stout underground stems may be up to 50 cm long, they are rather fleshy and the plant can form quite large patches, or lowish mounds, that may be more or less up to 2 m in diameter.

The leaves are quite distinctive, being bright green and shiny, prominently veined and kidney-shaped. They are on long stalks up to about 10 cm long, although often they are not noticeable because the stalks are buried in the sand. The leaf blade is broader than it is long, which emphasises its kidney shape. The typically convolvulus-shaped flowers are quite large for its size, being up to 4 cm in diameter, and are white striped with pink or purplish-pink. Flowering is usually during October–March, quite a long season. Its large seed pods form after flowering. They are brown, quite round or ovoid, about 2 cm in diameter, with a shortly pointed tip, and they sit within the remains of the papery flower bracts. Fruits appear in December–April.

Panahi is common in coastal sands around most of New Zealand's sandy shorelines, from the Kermadec Islands to the North, South, Stewart and Chatham Islands. Occasionally, it grows on stony or pebbly shores and it also grows on the sandy shores of Lake Taupo and other inland lakes of the North Island. It is a widespread species that also occurs in quite a number of other countries. Its seeds are able to withstand immersion in sea water for some months, thus aiding its dispersal by sea.

Calystegia soldanella is also known as sand convolvulus, sand bindweed, shore convolvulus, soldanella-like convolvulus (a partial translation of its scientific name), paneha and poue. The generic name *Calystegia* is from the Greek *kalyx*, a calyx, and *stegon*, a cover, in reference to the large bracts that conceal its calyx. Its specific name of *soldanella* is from the Latin, being a diminutive of *soldo*, a small coin, an allusion to its rounded leaves.

Powhiwhi

- Medium to tall climbing plant.

- Leaves thin texture, broadly heart-shaped.

Height: 4–6 m

Scientific Name:
Calystegia tuguriorum

Other Names:
(Maori)
pouwhiwhi;
native convolvulus

This species of native convolvulus is a common sight along some roadsides and in scrubland, and at a casual glance it may be confused with the common convolvulus or bindweed (*Calystegia silvatica*). *Calystegia tuguriorum* is typical of many of the species of *Convolvulus*, in as much as it has branched, creeping underground rhizomes, although they do not appear to be quite as aggressive as the common garden convolvulus. It can have masses of slender, branched climbing stems and is capable of ascending fairly high into forest trees.

The leaves of powhiwhi are on slender stalks up to about 4 cm long, the thinly textured leaf blade is broadly heart-shaped, 2–4 cm long by 2–3 cm wide, and its tip is sharply pointed. Its large, white flowers are typically convolvulus-shaped and up to 5 cm in diameter. The bracts that surround its calyx are broadly rounded and more or less of equal size. Occasionally, forms with pinkish flowers may be found. Generally, powhiwhi flowers in November–February. Its large brown seed capsules form after flowering. They are more or less 8 mm in diameter and contain yellowish-red seeds. The seed pods can be seen on the plant during December–April.

Powhiwhi grows on the Three Kings Islands and is common in lowland areas of the North, South, Stewart and Chatham Islands. It grows around forest margins, in scrublands and on roadside vegetation.

Calystegia tuguriorum is also known as pouwhiwhi, native convolvulus, New Zealand convolvulus, small bindweed and smaller bindweed. The specific name of *tuguriorum* is from the Latin *tugurium*, meaning of native or peasant huts, and was possibly intended to convey that this species was originally collected from plants growing over or around some Maori whares.

Teucridium parvifolium

Teucridium parvifolium is the sole New Zealand member of its genus and is confined to New Zealand. It is, along with the puriri (*Vitex lucens*), one of only two New Zealand members of the Lamiaceae, a large cosmopolitan plant family of over 3500 species worldwide.

Although found throughout both main islands, T. *parvifolium* is an inconspicuous shrub, and is not graced with a common name. It grows to about 1.5 m or so tall and is distinguished by having slender, yellowish branches and branchlets that are squarish in cross-section and only softly woody. It is quite twiggy and, depending upon where it is growing, may form a closely branched bush if in an open situation, or more openly branched when in a more heavily shaded site. Its branchlets diverge at rather wide angles.

The small leaves are usually quite widely spaced so that it never appears to be a particularly leafy shrub. They are on short stalks, roundish or somewhat spoon-shaped and about 4–12 mm long. Its small white flowers are produced from its leaf axils and may be either solitary or in small clusters. The flower is generally white but is said to be occasionally flushed with pale blue. Its lower lip consists of three lobes while the upper part has only two lobes, and it has four stamens that project outside the flower. Flowering is generally in October–January. Its brown seeds are formed inside the persistent flower calyx and there are normally four seeds from each flower.

Teucridium parvifolium is found in both the North and South Islands where it grows in lowland forests and shrublands, particularly in open forests and marginal vegetation. It occurs from about south of Kawhia and the Bay of Plenty to southern Otago. Among New Zealand's shrubby flora, T. *parvifolium* is unusual because its older stems tend to have a limited life and its new stems arise from ground level. The tutu (*Coriaria*) is one of the few other native shrubs to have this habit.

Teucridium is so named because of its resemblance to some members of the northern hemisphere genus *Teucrium*, which was possibly named after Teucer, the first king of ancient Troy. Its specific name *parvifolium* is from the Latin *parvus*, small, and *folius*, leaved, and refers to its small leaves.

Supplejack

Supplejack is a well-known species, its twining black stems familiar to most people who venture into our lowland forests. Interestingly, it was one of the first of our native plants to be given a common European name, the name being recorded in 1773 during Captain Cook's second voyage to New Zealand (1772–75). It may well have been some of his crew who invented the name of supplejack, a 'jack' being a sailor.

Supplejack's long, pliant and tough black stems have conspicuous 'knots' at the nodes, where its leaves have been, and in the forest the stems frequently form almost impenetrable, tangled masses. If the stems grow from a mature rhizome, they soon begin to twine and make their way up the nearest support, but, in full light, non-twining stems may arise from the long stems and they can be up to a metre long, and more branched.

The leaves, which may be seen only near the ends of its stems, are mainly opposite and more or less oval. They are thick, leathery and shiny. Each leaf is about 5.5–16 cm long by 2–6 cm wide and has a pointed tip. The flowers are produced from the tips of its branches as well as from the leaf axils. The stalks of its inflorescences are up to 15 cm long. Its small green flowers are loosely spaced and not crowded. Flowering usually occurs during December–January. Flowers are followed by its rounded, bright red fruits that are about 1 cm wide; their flesh is quite thin and usually they contain just one seed, sometimes two. Ripe fruits may be seen from March onwards and some may be observed throughout much of the year.

Ripogonum scandens occurs in lowland forests in the North, South, Stewart and Chatham Islands. It was first discovered by J.R. and J.G. Forster while on Cook's aforementioned voyage. Among its various names it is also known as kareao and pirita; the former name very appropriately translates as twisted rope.

Europeans made an extract from the root of the supplejack which was used to make a kind of sarsaparilla, while Maori also used parts of the plant for various medicinal purposes. Its fruits are edible but quite tasteless. In addition, its stems were used for various purposes such as the manufacture of eel traps and ladders for descending cliffs.

New Zealand calceolaria

Jovellana sinclairii belongs to a small genus of herbs and sub-shrubs that are restricted to New Zealand and Chile. We have two native species, both of which are endemic. The genus is closely related to *Calceolaria*, from which it differs in the two lips of its corolla being almost of the same size, whereas with *Calceolaria* the pouched lower lip is much larger than the upper one.

New Zealand calceolaria is not truly woody but the bases of its stems are slightly woody so that it is really more or less of a subshrub, and it is either sprawling or somewhat erect. For the large part it has rather soft, green growth and may attain about 30–45 cm in height. Its opposite leaves are on stalks up to 7 cm long; they are more or less oval, about 2.5–5 cm long by 2–3 cm wide, with upper surfaces pale green and paler beneath, and their margins coarsely toothed or lobed. The flowers are produced on inflorescences up to 15 cm long, which arise from the tips of its branches and have few to numerous flowers. Each flower is on a slender stalk up to 2 cm long and the individual flowers are about 1 cm in diameter; they are white, their insides slightly flushed with yellow and spotted with purple. The rather long flowering period may be October–February.

New Zealand calceolaria is found in coastal to lower montane districts of the North Island from near Hicks Bay to about Hawke's Bay and the Ruahine Range. It usually grows along stream-sides or forest margins and may also occur on moist road banks. The species ranges from sea level to about 450 m.

As with other plants that were of little importance to Maori, this species has never had a Maori name and has only ever managed to amass a few European names that, at the best, are rather pretentious. Its generic name *Jovellana* is in honour of Gaspar Melchor de Jovellanos, an 18th-century patron of botany from Peru. Its specific name *sinclairii* was given in honour of Dr Andrew Sinclair, a Scottish botanist and naval surgeon, who discovered it near Hicks Bay during the early 1840s.

Tutae-kiore

- Usually a low, shrubby plant.
- Much-branched inflorescences.

Height:
20–60 cm

Scientific Name:
Euphrasia cuneata

Other Names:
Eyebright;
(Maori) tutumako

Euphrasia cuneata is the largest of our native species of *Euphrasia* and may be recognised by its rather shrubby habit of growth, being reasonably woody at its base. Also, its inflorescences are much-branched.

Tutae-kiore is a herb or subshrub usually growing 20–60 cm tall and is much-branched from its base. Its wedge-shaped leaves are usually rather widely spaced; they are 5–20 mm long by 3–10 mm wide and have one to three pairs of teeth and a large terminal lobe at the tip. The leaves are somewhat thickened and usually their upper surfaces are slightly brownish. While the inflorescences are usually much-branched, sometimes they are reduced to a single stem. The flowers have two-lobed upper lips, the lobes of which turn upwards, and three-lobed lower lips that turn downwards. The flowers are about 1.5–2 cm long and are white with a yellow spot, while radiating out from the throat from both the upper and lower lips is a series of purple nectary lines. Flowering is in December–March but may continue on until about May.

Tutae-kiore occurs in the North Island from about East Cape and Lake Taupo to Mt Taranaki and then to the Marlborough Sounds in the South Island. It is found from coastal to low alpine regions where it may grow in subalpine scrub, red tussock associations, road banks and similar areas. The species ranges from sea level to about 1200 m.

Euphrasias are mainly semiparasitic on the roots of other plants, namely grasses and various herbs, although not a great deal is known of their life cycle in New Zealand. *Euphrasia cuneata* has had various common names bestowed on it including eyebright, New Zealand eyebright, tall eyebright and tutumako. The generic name is from the Greek *euphrasia*, meaning delight or mirth, and comes from *euphrainein*, to gladden, because the application of the plant to the eyes was supposed to brighten them, which gave rise to its English name of eyebright. Its specific name of *cuneata* means wedge-shaped and refers to the shape of the leaves.

172

Bibliography

Cockayne, L.C., *New Zealand Plants and their Story*, Government Printer: Wellington, 1967.

Crowe, Andrew, *Which Coastal Plant?*, Viking Press: Auckland, 1995.

Dawson, J. & Lucas, R., *Nature Guide to the New Zealand Forest*, Godwit: Auckland, 2000.

Eagle, A., *Eagle's Complete Trees and Shrubs of New Zealand*, 2 volumes, Te Papa Press: Wellington, 2006.

Metcalf, L.J., *New Zealand Trees and Shrubs*, Reed: Auckland, 2000.

Poole, L. & Adams, N.M., *Trees and Shrubs of New Zealand*, Department of Scientific and Industrial Research: Wellington, 1994.

Wilson, Hugh & Galloway, Tim, *Small-leaved Shrubs of New Zealand*, Manuka Press: Christchurch, 1993.

Index

abutilon, forest 160
aka 82
akakura 80, 82
akatawhiwhi 82
akatorotoro 82, 84
Anaphalis trinervis 154
arthropodium, white 14
Australian sea holly 126
bamboo orchid 36
beach spinach 62
begonia
  native 104
  New Zealand 104
bindweed
  shore 162
  small 164
  smaller 164
black

scrub 146
  vine 66, 68
blueberry 24
box rata 84
bride's bouquet 34
broad-leaved sedge 40
broom
  desert 100
  native 100
bulrush 30
bush
  flax 18
  lawyer 92, 94, 96
  lily 18
  snowberry 130
calceolaria, New Zealand 170
celery 124

Maori 124
native 124
New Zealand 124
prostrate 124
sea 124
Christmas orchid 36
chuckie chucks 130
Clematis
  cunninghamii 48
  foetida 48
clematis, leafless 46
climbing rata 84
common
  libertia 32
  mistletoe 108
convolvulus
  native 164
  New Zealand 164

sand 162
  shore 162
  soldanella-like 162
Coprosma rhamnoides 148
coprosma, twiggy 148
Corokia cotoneaster 122
corokia, wiry 122
creeping gunnera 72
desert broom 100
dwarf kowhai 102
earina
  fragrant 34
  sweet-scented 34
Easter orchid 34
elatostema, wrinkled 104
eryngium, vesiculate 126
eryngo 126
eyebright 172
  New Zealand 172
  tall 172
false beech snowberry 130
flax 28
  bush 18
  mountain 26
  New Zealand 28
forest abutilon 160
fragrant earina 34
glasswort 70
glossy karamu 144
gloxinia, New Zealand 160
golden
  sand sedge 38
  tainui 114
green mistletoe 112
gumdigger's soap 114
Gunnera prorepens 72
gunnera, creeping 72
hangehange 136
harakeke 28
Hibiscus diversifolius 86
holly
  Australian sea 126
  sea 126
horokaka 60
horopito 44
  red 44
hupiro 142

ice plant
  Maori 60
  native 60
  New Zealand 60
inakaporiro / inangaporiro 132
iris, New Zealand 32
jasmine
  Maori 140
  New Zealand 138, 140
kahakaha 22
kahikahika 82
kaihua 140
kaikaiatua 160
kakaha 18
kakaramu 144, 150
karamu 144, 150
  glossy 144
  shining 144
karamuramu 144
karangu 144, 150
kareao 168
kawakawa 54
koheriki 128
kohuorangi 112
kokihi 62
koro 84
koropeka 130
korukoru 110
kowhai
  dwarf 102
  prostrate 102
kowharawhara 20
kumarahou 114
  prostrate 116
lady's slipper 36
lawyer 92
  bush 92, 94, 96
  leafless 98
leafless
  clematis 46
  lawyer 98
libertia, common 32
lily
  bush 18
  reinga 16
  renga 16

rock 16
  star 14
  tank 22
  tree bush 20
maakoako 156
maikaka 16
Maori
  celery 124
  ice plant 60
  jasmine 140
  water-pimpernel 156
marsh pimpernel 156
matata 160
mattress plant 68
Melicytus novae-zelandiae 58
mikimiki 5, 132, 134, 146
mikoikoi 32
mingimingi 5, 132, 134, 146
  prickly 132
mistletoe
  common 108
  green 112
  scarlet-flowered 110
mountain flax 26
nardoo berry 130
native
  begonia 104
  broom 100
  celery 124
  convolvulus 164
  ice plant 60
nettle, tree 106
New Zealand
  begonia 104
  calceolaria 170
  celery 124
  convolvulus 164
  eyebright 172
  flax 28
  gloxinia 160
  ice plant 60
  iris 32
  jasmine 138, 140
  privet 136
  spinach 62
ngakau-kiore 48
ngarangara 60

niniao 152
ongaonga 106
orchid
    bamboo 36
    Christmas 36
    Easter 34
panahi 162
paneha 162
papahenga 136
parataniwha /
    parataniwhaniwha 104
pepepe 40
Peperomia urvilleana 52
pepper tree 44, 54
pig's face 60
pimpernel, marsh 156
pingao 9, 38
pirinoa 108, 112
pirita 108, 110, 112, 168
Pittosporum divaricatum 78
poapoa tautaua 140
poataniwha 118
pohuehue 66, 68
Pomaderris prunifolia var.
    edgerleyi 116
porcupine bush 56
poue 162
pouwhiwhi 164
Poverty Bay weed 114
powhiwhi 162
prickly mingimingi 132
primrose, sea 156
privet, New Zealand 136
prostrate
    celery 124
    kowhai 102
    kumarahou 116
puarangi 88
puawananga /
    puawhananga 50
puka 66
rata
    box 84
    climbing 80, 84
rata vine, scarlet 82
raumangu 158
raupeka 34
raupo 30

red horopito 44
reinga lily 16
rekoreko 158
remuremu 158
renga lily 16
rengarenga 16
repehinapapa 14
rock lily 16
ruerueke 60
sand convolvulus 162
scarlet rata vine 82
scarlet-flowered mistletoe
    110
scrub, black 146
sea
    celery 124
    holly 126
    primrose 156
sea holly, small 126
sedge
    broad-leaved 40
    golden sand 38
shining karamu 144
shore
    bindweed 162
    convolvulus 162
    shrubby tororaro 64
small
    bindweed 164
    sea holly 126
smaller bindweed 164
snowberry
    bush 130
    false beech 130
soldanella-like
    convolvulus 162
spinach
    beach 62
    New Zealand 62
star lily 14
stinkwood 142
supplejack 168
sweet-scented earina 34
taapia 112
takapo 130
tall eyebright 172
tank lily 22
taramoa 92

taranga 74
tataraheke 92
tataramoa 92, 94, 96, 98
taumingi 132
taurepo 160
tawhiwhi 140
tawiniwini 130
Teucridium parvifolium 166
toetoe 42
toetoe kakaho 42
toetoe makoro 42
toetoe rakau 42
toetoe tuhara 40
tororaro 68
    shrubby 64
tree
    bush lily 20
    nettle 106
tuhara 40
tukauki 32
tumingi 132, 134
tupia 112
turutu 24, 32
tutae kereru 140
tutae-kiore 172
tutaekoau 124
tutumako 172
twiggy coprosma 148
twiggywood 120
vesiculate eryngium 126
vine, black 66, 68
waiuatua 160
waiu-atua 90
water-pimpernel, Maori
    156
whakapiopio 84
wharariki 26
wharewhareatua 76
white arthropodium 14
wiggy-bush 68
winika 36
wiry corokia 122
wrinkled elatostema 104